A. GRATTON.

The book of the
WOOD STOVE

The book of the
WOOD STOVE

Keith Williams

David & Charles
Newton Abbot   London

Drawings by Evelyn Bartlett

British Library Cataloguing in Publication Data

Williams, Keith
  The book of the wood stove.
  1. Stoves, Wood
  2. Wood as fuel – Great Britain – Heating and
  ventilation
  I. Title
  644'.1   TH437   80–40272

  ISBN 0–7153–7926–7

Typeset by Northern Phototypesetting Company, Bolton and
printed in Great Britain
by Redwood Burn Limited, Trowbridge and Esher
for David & Charles (Publishers) Limited
Brunel House Newton Abbot Devon

CONTENTS

INTRODUCTION:
WHY WOOD IS GOOD

A book of this kind should start with a personal declaration. You are entitled to know where I stand. You will want to judge how reliable my arguments are, and to what degree I allow natural enthusiasm to sway the balance of my critical faculty.

I am a recent convert to wood burning. Like all converts, I find the heady zest of a new idea is a powerful stimulus. I plunge in and thrash around. In part, one is trying to persuade oneself of the rightfulness and importance of one's own conversion.

When I lived in California I gave not a second's thought to the question of fuel. It was something that came into the house. One turned a tap or switch and it was there. My apartment was heated by a thermostatically controlled natural-gas central-heating unit. This was so automatic and unobtrusive one forgot it was there. No one ever thought to switch it off when the stabbing heat of summer came. When, for three months, I made a tour of the globe, the unit was left running. On my return it was still sturdily belching out warm air in the chill hours of the night. Extravagance came cheaply in those days. Natural gas in California was so abundant and cheap that the entire bill, during my absence, was something under $5 (about £1.75 as money was then).

My adoption of coal as a fuel was painful and dramatic. I returned to England just in time to catch the first freezing blasts of the long winter of 1962–3. I had moved into an eighteenth-century cottage on a village green in Hampshire. Snow smothered us. Water pipes froze deep in the ground. For three days my car was marooned in the driveway just 10 feet from the garage but as remote from it as if the distance had been ten miles.

Fresh, as I was, from California, my memories of those sharp, blood-chilled months are of doors and windows desperately rammed shut and of inadequate electric fires kept burning day and night.

The spring came and I leapt determinedly into the premises of my nearest stockist of coal-burning stoves. Haunted by the size of my winter electricity bill, I opted for the cheapest alternative. And not to be caught out again, I installed the largest model available, fitting a back boiler from which hot water was pumped to six large radiators. The next winter the old cottage crisped its way through the cold days, the wood frame cracking with the unaccustomed dryness and warmth. The fire did not go out day or night. The stove had a glass front to it, and I discovered a truth that I suspect can be dated back to those shaggy prehistoric men who lit brush fires at their cave entrances. Heating is like justice: for it to reach its fullest flowering, not only must it be done, it must be seen to be done. For me, a fire unseen is a fire only partly felt. Unreasonable, perhaps, but true.

Urbanisation crept closer to the village and the charms of Hampshire palled. I wanted a simpler way of life with simpler satisfactions. The West Country seemed to offer this and I settled into a late Victorian house with access to neglected woodlands.

That was the moment of illumination. How, I argued, could one be surrounded by woods and not use them? And I intended 'use' to be in the broadest sense.

Woods can be walked through. They harbour natural creatures. If I allowed my romantic side full rein I could easily wallow in the nobility of woods and the majesty of trees. But I knew also that trees grow and must be cut down. And that wood burns.

Obviously, I should install wood-burning stoves. Once again I was selecting the cheapest option. But, who sold these stoves and where could information about them be found? It was as if a conspiracy of silence enshrouded the subject. Later, I found it was simply indifference.

Wood stoves were known to exist. But where? Persons to

7

whom one was recommended as knowing about these things proved, when contacted, only to know of them through a friend of a friend. These friends of friends produced, when asked, even more remote chains of friends. But it was eventually through one of these tortuous connections that a man who both sold and stocked wood stoves swung into view. The distinction is an important one. Many merchants were willing to accept orders, waving vividly coloured brochures but without stocking samples.

The store, when I got there, turned out to be the remote country bungalow where he lived. His stock of stoves was kept in his garage while his car stood unsheltered outside. But at least they were real. One of them was actually burning. For the first time it was possible to grasp the reality of wood heat.

The three different designs of stove we bought have now been installed and working for more than six months. Just as when I came from California, nature has flung herself at my throat to put me to the test. As I write in 1979, I have lived through the worst winter in these parts for 30 years – some of the older farmers claim it is the worst one within their living memory.

With the minimum of preparation, with no opportunity to air-dry wood, the wood stoves have kept going through all these piercing months. Twice the house has been snow-bound. Often it has been necessary to get through snow and ice before cutting the daily quota of wood. When the timber has been both rotten and sodden, it has had to be dried on top of a stove before being burnt in it. Yet the heat has kept pouring out. The internal temperature has seldom dropped below 70°F, often it has sizzled above 80°F. To a heat-loving mortal, as I am, this is impressive. It is something not to be ignored, for, apart from the labour of cutting the wood, dragging it back to the house, sawing it and stacking it in fire baskets, the fuel bill for this winter is practically zero. No dark shadow of future cost has inhibited me when I have been tempted to fling more billets on the fire to wring a more blistering hiss from the radiators fed from the back boiler.

Next winter, with the parching months of summer ahead during which wood can be cut and air-dried and stacked, I shall do better.

So that is where I start – an unabashed advocate with half a year's hard experience, but whose investigations will extend and deepen as this book progresses. As you read it, I hope you will feel that you have a share in both successes and failures. For my part, wherever practicable, I shall advance only things seen with my own eyes or done with my hands.

Is there truly very much to be said on the subject of burning wood as fuel? One burns fuel and heat results. Does it make much difference what fuel is burned, whether it be coal, gas or oil? If my researches thus far had led me to that conclusion then I agree this book could be wound up within a few pages. But it seems to me not to be true.

As evidence of that I would invite you to pause from your reading and glance out of your window. Can you see any trees? Do you see a single tree? If you don't, then I think the time is ripe for me to introduce a penetrating chill of unease to encase your heart. I shall do it, as I warned you, with an extreme statement. Your world is likely to be teetering on the brink of disorder, dissolution and destruction. Splendid alliteration. But can I make the thought stand up?

Press your hand to your chest. Feel the rhythmic rise and fall. If the flow of air to your lungs, and from them, the dissolving of oxygen into your bloodstream, should stop for even a few instants, you will die.

Oxygen is present in the air and is just as finite a resource as oil in the ground. There is only just so much of it. One day, you could suppose, it will be used up.

That would be true were it not recycled by trees and plants, which by photosynthesis, use sunlight to convert water and carbon dioxide into glucose sugar. In the process free oxygen is given off to the air. Trees are important to us.

Before you settle down to this book again, have another quick glance from your window. We have checked on the status of trees. How about chimneys? Factory chimneys in particular. Can you see any? Whatever belches from them you can be sure it is not the source of life. Rather the opposite. Factory processes not only use up vital oxygen, they deposit in the atmosphere increasing quantities of, among many other dangerous and unpleasant substances, carbon dioxide. Many scientists now claim that because of a build up of atmospheric carbon dioxide and a rundown of the earth's oxygen, the world's air temperature will rise steadily. Even an average rise of only five degrees is enough to change temperate zones to desert and make inhabited regions unbearably hot. If we don't suffocate ourselves to death we may do it by frying.

Another of those extreme statements – from wood stoves to sci-fi drama. But I wanted to make the point that what stands between us and choking or gasping termination is, in part, a global army of trees.

And here am I proposing that they be cut down! A grotesque contradiction, you will think. Another author losing his marbles. Not at all. A wood or forest is a living community of trees. Like all communities, the up-and-coming new generations thrive on the death of the old. The one has to make way for the other. A simple law of nature, and one so fundamental that if it does not operate the community will wither and decline. The rising young saplings struggling to lift their slender branches towards the nourishing sun will be stifled by the overhanging dead limbs of unfallen old trees. That is why foresters cut down the old stuff. To give growing room to the young.

This cutting is not wild and unrestrained. So long as no more wood is cut than will be replaced by natural growth, nothing but good comes from this cutting. The community of trees is not depleted, it is enhanced, made stronger, amplified.

Trees are generally felled to supply wood for particular industrial purposes. Usually, only about 60 per cent of the tree is used. The remaining 40 per cent is wasted, and is burnt on site unless there is some other demand for it. Such wood is ideal for stove burning. We cannot afford to be so improvident.

All energy sources derive from the sun. The earth derives from the sun, being flung from it by some cosmic explosion into space. The mass of molten rock cooled and hardened into the globe we inhabit. The sun continues to radiate energy to us. The fossil fuels that come from this radiation – oil, gas, coal – sooner or later will run out. Predictions differ when this will happen. Informed opinions agree it will happen. The modern touchstone is nuclear fuel. That depends on uranium, a source material as finite and limited as fossil fuel. It too, one day, will run out. Meanwhile, there are the difficulties of storing and handling it, and disposing of dangerous radio-active waste.

Energy can come from hydro-electric development, which is fine if you have enough water for the sun to soak up for you and drop as rain. Energy can come from the tides, from wind and wave motion. Not, as yet, efficiently. But technical advancement will bring improvements.

But, you will argue, if man's energy comes from the sun, why not concentrate on the primary source? That, eventually, may be the answer, but not at present. The best solar energy extraction systems – solar panels and the like – utilise no more than 8 per cent of the available power. Domestic installations scale even lower. The equipment is expensive. There are maintenance problems. You don't get enough out to justify what you put in.

It can be argued that photosynthesis in plants and trees is even less efficient. Leaves absorb about 1 per cent of the sun's energy. But photosynthesis costs nothing. Solar panel installations cost – I was going to say, the earth – but certainly a substantial proportion thereof.

Other fuel sources are being investigated. Liquid hydrogen is one. Plenty of it, but bulky to transport and more dangerous than propane or butane gas. Methane is another, the theory being that vast stores of it lie buried deep in the earth's crust, a relic of that remote sequence that transformed the world from flaming liquid substance to cooler, solid rock. But the theory is all we have to warm us. No pockets of the deep-lying fuel have been found. Even if they were, could they be worked from such depths? No one knows.

Yet we have all this wood. You have been told that the world's stocks of it have been seriously depleted. Those who have studied the matter don't think so. D. E. Earl, in a most important book *Forest Energy and Development*, states that:

> The reserve of energy held by forests is more than twenty times greater than the world's current annual consumption of energy

from all sources and the world's forests incorporate solar energy into organic material, from which can be obtained solid, liquid and gaseous fuels at an annual rate far in excess of the world's present economic needs.

I can reinforce that view with one from the locality where I live. It is the opinion of the Forestry Commission that the problem in using the wasted 40 per cent of felled trees as useful fuel is an economic one rather than because of any shortage of supply. There is enough wood to satisfy any foreseeable demand. What is lacking is money. The profitable rate for lop and top would currently be about £18 per tonne. The market offers a scrap rate of only up to £12. So, mostly the smaller wood is left to rot or be burnt on site. Only the most accessible is extracted.

A thriving wood-fuel market would solve that. Cynics will point out that I am advocating a price rise. So I am. If that makes available a fuel that otherwise does not get used, I am in favour of it. The cost would be well below that of conventional fuels. Wood has about half the calorific value of coal, it takes twice the quantity of wood to supply the same heat. But, if wood costs only about a third of the cost of coal it is still a good buy. £54 per tonne is an average price for ordinary coal. Smokeless fuels come higher.

There lies another nail to hammer home. Won't wood smoke pollute the atmosphere? You might suppose so from the text of the Clean Air Act of 1969 which prohibits the lighting of domestic fires with wood sticks and paper in Smoke Control Areas. But the monstrous prejudice in this can be judged by the routine exemptions. Among these is the burning of tar, pitch asphalt and other matter 'in connection with the preparation and laying of any surface, or which is burnt off any surface in connection with resurfacing, together with any fuel used for any such purpose'. The volumes of foul smelling smoke that come from this make the term 'Clean Air' laughable.

As I write, my study is heated by a small box stove. It burns wood that I carried in from the woods and sawed yesterday. It is dead wood and not green, but it is air damp. The morning sun casts the shadows of our chimneys across the wall of the barn. I can see, yes, a wisp of smoke. A stranger walking past would have a hard time judging if my fire was alight or not. Is this pollution?

It can be argued that wood cannot pollute the atmosphere more than it is polluted naturally. Rotting reverses the process by which wood grows. Decay uses up atmospheric oxygen and exudes carbon dioxide and water. Rotting wood turns slowly warm. (To be strictly accurate, a few other compounds are involved as well – but what I have described is the main action.) Burning is fast rotting, a speeded-up version of what happens as wood lies decomposing on the ground. Fires suck in oxygen, and thrust out carbon dioxide and water, and energy in the form of heat and light. This energy came originally from the sun making trees into excellent solar panels. Solar heat has been locked, through photosynthesis, into various complex chemical combinations. Burning breaks these locks and lets the sun's heat out.

The roar through the damper from the corner of my study and the comforting surge of heat against my back signal to me that this process is well in hand in my box fire. If it were duplicated in a million such fires across the nation, and proportionately throughout the centrally heated world and continued so for the next two or three generations, or for however long that might be necessary, time would be won for all those eager scientists to explore and secure for us the production of energy from the other methods on which man seems bent on pinning his warmest hopes for the future. The forests that came alive in this activity would return the earth to the balanced ecology of carbon dioxide converted to oxygen.

A rosy-leafed dream, you will judge, for someone who lives, as I do, in an over-urbanised nation with a bare $5\frac{1}{2}$ million acres of forest and woodland remaining. Yet even this is a decent enough base for forward planning. An acre of oak grows on average a tonne of new wood each year. If we assume that present needs will take up 60 per cent of this, 40 per cent remains usable as firewood. This might supply, theoretically, about half a million homes. An EEC study suggests that Britain's forest acreage could and should be doubled. My

13

suggestion that a million UK households could be wood fuelled is not a mere wood-burner's dream. There is substance in the ash. Of course, not all the present woodland grows suitable wood. Nor is all of it accessible. But the potential is there.

Something called the new silviculture is raising its head, a new technology for growing more trees, faster. Previously, fast growth has been associated with conifers, but these are soft woods, not ideal for stove burning. Nor do conifers usually coppice.

Investigations are being made into fast-growing hard woods. Some results are already spectacular. Southern Beech – *Nothofagus procera* and *obliqua* – has been imported from Chile. Growth tables published in 1974 show yields of over 45 feet in 15 years. A private grower in Dorset has had even more striking success with types of Eucalyptus tree. One has grown 42 feet in 10 years.

Furthermore, forestry is not a labour-intensive industry. It is less affected by inflationary pressures than other works. As time advances, supposing the wood market to expand, the comparison with other fuels is likely to become more favourable.

Smoke in the sky, you will counter. And I don't resent that, optimism can be an expensive luxury.

Yet it can be imagined what prices the conventional fuels will have reached by the end of the century. Coal will be dominated by Champagne Charlie miners. Shrinking oil will be as expensive and rare as Chanel No. 5. Gas in the pipes will be as thin as outer space, cheques to pay for it will be as large as NASA's budget. Those doing business installing the alternative technologies will be waxing fat.

My wood will still be going on. You can't stop wood, except by killing it. Nor do woodlands seem to attract usurious instincts. There is hope that foresters and forest-land owners will not be infected by the grab canker.

These thoughts persuade me that an investment in a wood-producing enterprise is sound national policy. Any house-holder who finds his circumstances permit the reasonable use of wood fuel does himself a favour if he strikes the match to do so.

What kind of wood burning stove should he choose? And what kind of fuel could be burnt in it? It is somewhat to be regretted that the makers of wood stoves have been overwhelmed by the present nostalgic euphoria.

The log-in-the-hearth image releases in the mind distant memories of simpler and more satisfying days. Nonsense, of course. There never were good old days. Those who lived them thought themselves to be caught up in webs as foul and unfathomable as those of today. Wood persons, above all, should keep their roots in the ground.

Wood burning does not, and cannot, compete with the at-the-touch-of-a-button philosophy of home heating being peddled in the media by our nationalised fuel industries. Nor, to strike the proper balance, is wood burning the back-breaking labour that once doubled up the domestics in our basements. It is something between – modestly convenient yet needing a modest effort.

The probable truth is that the technology of wood-stove design has barely advanced in the past two hundred years (with one exception; see pages 84–6). Very likely it has made no move at all in the past hundred. When Ben Franklin designed the stove that still carries his name in America, and when Count Rumford, after the Revolutionary War, produced the grate that bears his name, they formulated principles of wood-stove design that are still being followed. Internal baffles to produce secondary burning are at least a century and a half old, as are bi-metallic strips as heat controls. The air-tight stove is a little younger, but of venerable heritage.

What has changed are quality controls in the best methods of manufacture, and more unconventional ideas about the placing of stoves in the home. The wood-stove market divides neatly down the middle. On the plus side, stoves that are almost indestructable. Competing with them are tin plate defectors with a short life span, if a hot one. (This is not a reference to modern welded steel-plate stoves, which are as solid and reliable as cast iron models.)

One difficulty the honest designer of wood stoves has is that, unlike his counterparts working on coal, oil and gas units, he has no idea what kind of fuel his brain-child will be consuming. Of course, he knows it will be wood. But of what grade, type and size? There is no standard quality or shape for wood billets and the wood-stove designer has to keep as many options open as possible.

To some degree it is possible to envisage a standard wood-burning tree being of a certain girth, density and height. But, as with all wood cutting, there would still be waste. It is here that inventive technologists could help. What is wanted is a solution to a problem that has bedevilled wood burners for centuries – what to do with the unburnable waste?

Felling, coppicing, pollarding and the ordinary routines of woodland life result in quantities of twigs, wood scraps and dust. The amount is considerable. In the wood where I cut my fuel, scraps on the ground weigh between $\frac{1}{2}$ to 1 kilogramme per square metre – something over 9 tonnes to the hectare. The modest 3 hectares I work have 27 tonnes of fuel I cannot use. Nationally, this is a massive total.

Not all of it is available as fuel, of course. Some will rot into the ground as a mulch for future growth. About half could be used. But how?

Shredding machines exist – made in America – that break up small pieces of wood into strips suitable for composting. These are not ideal for burning, unless you are prepared to sit by your fire feeding them in as a continuous flow. Wood-scrap can be pulped but only with the addition of water that makes the resulting mush unburnable.

Some technique between these two is needed. I have made a few experiments myself, breaking the pieces down almost to dust, mixing in a little domestic plaster and hand-moulding to form wood patties. These burn moderately well, although the small moisture content needed for moulding has to be driven off before a good heat flow results. And the considerable labour involved in doing all this is not justified by the relatively small amount of additional heat produced. Yet the fuel is there in bulk, just waiting to be picked up. If someone can devise a way of processing it that is not labour intensive, a small fortune awaits them.

16

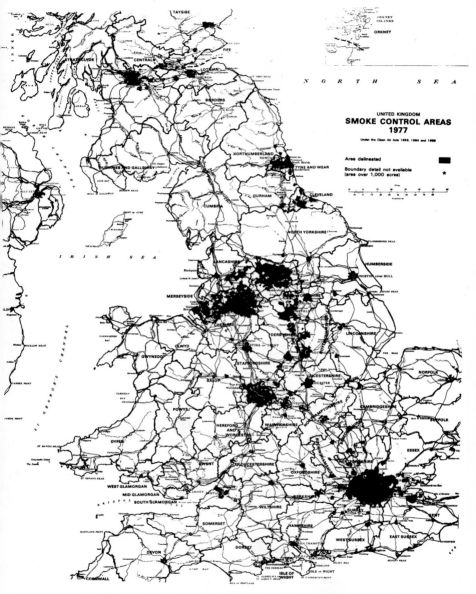

Smoke Control Areas in the United Kingdom in 1977

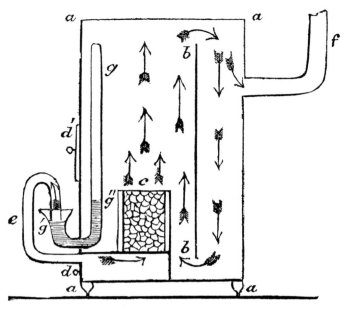

(*above*) Dr Arnott's stove as it appeared in *The Saturday Magazine*, 31 March 1838; (*below*) Jøtul 118

A good many are trying. A bibliography prepared by the Timber Research and Development Association under the title *Wood Waste as Fuel* lists 31 studies of the subject. These range from 'Wood waste briquetting plant' (A. B. Gibbons, *Timber Technology*, May 1953), and 'The potential of wood residue as a source of electrical energy' (*Forest Industries*, November 1973), to 'Uses for sawdust, shavings and wood chips' (J. M. Harkin, *U.S. Forest Products Laboratory*, 1971).

Brought up in a coal regimen, the ready ignitability of wood surprises me. Yet, on reflection, this is something I have long known. As a boy it was my job to chop firewood. Every Sunday, as a special treat, the coal fire in the living-room was lit. On a bed of paper screws, fire wood was criss-crossed, supporting a pyramid of small coal. The method was to stretch tightly across the fireplace several pages thickness of the Sunday paper to improve the draught through the gap left at the base of the hearth. Behind the newsprint the flames raced and danced. Occasionally they caught the paper alight. Frantically, this was released to swoop away up the chimney in a cascade of blazing fragments.

So, the combustible quality of wood has long been known to me. It was used, patiently, to coax a corner of coal to a red glow. Then another, until a hot bed of fire had spread on which more coal could be fed with care. Half an hour was thought a good time to get a fire going. Often, it took double that time.

After the war, when I had my own fires to light, more brutal methods prevailed. Fires were not so much cajoled into flame as harried and bullied. Blunt gas pokers were thrust into the mute coal. Raw heat thrashed the black fragments until submissively they flamed.

Then came chemical firelighters, small blocks of waxy white paraffin, which urged the coal to fire with hot persuasion. On good days, four would be sufficient to bring the fire to room warmth in an hour. When bad days struck, six would still not have raised the fire above a spluttering glow after two hours. In those years, the firing quality of wood was overlooked.

Now that I have caught up with it again, my ideas about house fires have been radically modified. Many are peculiar to me and not generally applicable. I put them down so that a pattern of thought can be examined and evaluated.

My previous home was heated by coal. It burnt in a modern, glass-fronted stove – my mania for needing to see the fire – behind which was a back boiler. Hot water was fed to six radiators. This fire was lit in mid-November and stayed alight, day and night, until the end of March. The brick of the old inglenook fireplace in which it was installed acted as a vast heat store during those months, remaining warm to the touch throughout.

Overnight, the fire was made up and damped down. The electric pump supplying the radiators was switched off. The heat outflow was minimal, being used, in the main, to keep up the stock of warmth in the fireplace bricks.

The glass-fronted wood stove I now have also claims to stay in overnight. So it will. But at a cost.

The points I am about to raise, I shall discuss more fully in a later chapter. Now I shall just exhibit the bare bones.

Slow-burning wood throws out tar and ash, which coat the inside of the fire chamber and obscures the glass. Tar deposits and condensation occur in the chimney, which, thereby, has to be cleaned more often. With these important disadvantages, one asks, what exactly is the point of keeping the fire alight?

Two reasons seem paramount. The fire is kept alight to sustain heat in the house, and *to avoid having to relight it each morning*. Let us examine these. What keeps house heat up to a minimal level? Experience with the overnight coal fire demonstrates that it is not, directly, the heat of the slow burning fire. Rather it is the keeping up of heat stored in the fireplace brick.

My present wood-fired home is built of slate, with walls more than 2 feet thick. These are excellent heat stores. I have measured the overnight heat loss in these. It amounts to a reduction in temperature of about 2°F compared with keeping the fire alight. So the disadvantages of the overnight wood fire are endured for a mere two degrees of warmth.

The second point has even less substance. Clearly, it is a throwback to the old coal methodology where one does not want to have to relight the fire when that task is so long drawn out and difficult. With wood this is not the case. A few screws of newspaper, two scatterings of twigs on these, topped by dry billets and my wood fire is reliably alight and throwing out heat in under five minutes. The thick slate fire surround is still warm to the touch from the night before. Because I can keep the fire flaming hot I avoid condensation and tarry deposits.

Suppose I go out during the day, will I not want to come home to a warm house? Of course. But so long as there is a regular input of heat into the house for some continuous hours each day, the house remains warm. Its insulation keeps it so. The wood fire can be damped down to moderate heat to stay in for three to four hours or so. Or, it can be allowed to go out and be relit.

To central heating addicts, this is a major heresy. But is it so unrealistic? In an energy hungry world, is there not an obligation for us to re-examine our concepts of comfort, convenience *and cost* to see where the best balance lies? Even in open-plan houses, where there is less inhibition against movement from one part of the house to another, volumes are kept heated although they are not used, or are under used. Utilising the structure of the house as a heat store allows one to produce heat with average convenience – or inconvenience, if you prefer – and maximum thrift. It is not push-button heat. But it is cheap. And effective.

Rearings of heads are likely to take place here, and mutterings to be heard of retrograde steps. I don't think so. North Americans have a reputation for a certain genial practicality. Whimsey and nostalgia are not, ordinarily, part of their life style. They strike through to the rugged core of what works, so that when one comes across staggering evidences of impracticality, there has to be a reason.

Some years ago I visited the home of rich persons in the Californian desert hinterland. The ambient temperature was over 100°F. Inside the house a powerful air conditioning unit kept the living area temperature down in the seventies. As dusk came and waves of heat throbbed in from the bare sand, there came a further twitch of the switch. The inside temperature went down and down into the low forties. A sigh of satisfaction came from my hosts. It was now cold enough inside the house *to light a log fire!*

During the past four years well over a million homes in the USA have installed wood stoves. The trend continues. Official studies are being made of the nation's wood fuel resources. The total of 754 million acres (i.e., about 29 per cent of the nation's land area), it is estimated, will supply the fuel for America's 75 million homes. Just over 10 acres per household. Somewhat higher than would be the requirement here, but then America's energy consumption has grown to be prodigal. A present listing shows 54 companies making wood burning equipment of varying kinds.

Yearning for wood fires is an American heritage. When the Pilgrim Fathers settled, wood was the abundant fuel that saw them through the first grim winter. Grim winters are still a reality there, especially in the central plains. The winter of 1972–3 was one. It chanced I was researching a project in Omaha. The Nebraskan temperature, I noted with sour relish, was lower than that at the North Pole.

It was the time of America's first fuel crisis. Oil wells in Texas and California were being pumped dry. Imports from the Middle East were uncertain and expensive. Every day, on radio, television, in the papers, the authorities exhorted every household to set its thermostat no higher than 68°F. Most did, and suffered. Even when there are 70 degrees of frost outside, 68 degrees of invisible heat inside do not feel warm. One sat before the television set for the evening and one's knees locked with numb cold.

Those who did not suffer were the remote households in the sticks, who burnt twigs and logs.

When the winter ended that fact did not pass unnoticed. Since then there has been a steady revival of interest in wood fires among contemporary Americans. Manufacturers have been dusting off the castings of a century back and getting traditional Franklin and pot-belly stoves back into production and modern imports are flooding in from Europe.

A similar trend can be seen in Canada, although there only

20 per cent of wood-burning equipment is of home manufacture, the remainder being imported from the USA and Europe. Canadian Government interest is already apparent. The Department of Energy, Mines and Resources, and the Central Mortgage and Housing Corporation are sharing the cost of a study to measure the efficiency of different types of wood stove. The tests are being conducted at the Canadian Combustion Research Laboratories near Ottawa. The appliances under test include box stoves, traditional and modern Franklin stoves from America, circulating wood heaters and the so-called combi or combination stove that functions as both an open hearth and as an airtight heater.

Many other organisations are also taking an interest in wood fuel, apart from the federal government. The Canadian Wood Energy Institute, the Canadian Standards Association, the Insurance Bureau of Canada and the Insurers' Advisory Organization of Canada are also active. This, you will judge, is to be expected in a country as thickly wooded as Canada.

But even with the oilphoria of North Sea supplies, can Britain afford to stand by and ignore this alternative fuel? I repeat, if wood energy replaced as little as 5 per cent of the domestic market, the impact would be powerful.

What interest is being shown in wood, here in Britain? The Fifty-fourth Annual Report of the Commonwealth Forestry Institute lists a good deal of research activity towards generating greater wood supplies at home and in the developing countries. The Atomic Energy Research Establishment is making a survey of all fuel sources, including wood. The Research and Development Division of the Forestry Commission has an experimental programme studying more rapid wood growth. The Centre for Agricultural Strategy at Reading University is investigating where the land for additional tree planting might come from. Land not suitable for any other purpose can often support trees. And there are many other investigations of matching value that it would be tedious to list here. All the evidence suggests that if and when that 5 per cent call came, the wood would be available.

The idea seems to have penetrated most informed layers of

opinion, except those of government. Very little has seeped through there. No national programme exists. No sense of urgency prevails. Research is parched for money.

In his book *Energy* Mitchell Wilson reflects a common educated concern:

> With the world's consumption of fuel energy increasing at an astronomical rate, man is overtaxing the organic fuel sources he depends on so heavily now – coal, petroleum, wood, agricultural wastes. The use of these fuels in the last century alone amounted to almost half the total used in all the preceding 19 centuries; consumption is now expected to double and then double again before the year 2000.

To put that thought in a British context, we must discover another entire North Sea oil region every two years. Globally, man must bring into service another Mexico every three years.

No one is going to suggest that wood is the sole answer. Man must exercise every option. What can be argued is that wood is an immediately available resource, and one that, unlike the traditional fuels, can be replaced. Equally unlike the fossil fuels, burning wood is a pleasant experience that has a useful impact on the environment.

Wood, you might say, in all senses, gives us breathing space.

1

WOOD NEAR YOUR HOME?

Installing a wood stove is like trying to get into an exclusive club. At first you don't know any of the members. It seems that your application must be accompanied by the recommendations of two of them. You have to rub up acquaintance with some of them until two are prepared to back your application. Even then you aren't in. An application form quizzes you about various of your personal opinions in case anything in your background or persona would be distasteful to the club in general. Your social standing is investigated. A reference is sought from your bank manager. Finally you are interviewed by three members of the club committee. Your membership application then goes forward to the agenda of the next full committee meeting. It is voted on. You must secure a minimum of 60 per cent voting for you to gain entry. During all this time, you are on the outside wanting to get in. And, if you believe their sincere protestations, they want you in. It is just that, for the time being, you can't get in.

Anyone trying to put a wood stove into his home feels like that. The idea of having one is good. So many persons confirm that it is good. But for the time being you cannot have one. Short-cutting these entry problems is the reason for producing this book. In particular, this chapter will argue a case for and against having a wood stove in particular circumstances.

Earlier, I aired the problem of finding a merchant who actually stocks the models in which you are interested. The brochure lads are legion. But the hardcore, with stoves installed, at the ready, on the go, with wood burning are tough to find. Even researching for this book, I have often had to motor more than 100 miles to find a particular model. Even then, some suppliers seem suspicious of one's motives in daring to ask to see a stove alight. One establishment I visited, it shall be nameless, had unlit models on display in a gas-heated showroom. There was not any kind of flue to which they could be connected for purposes of demonstration. Really, you do sometimes feel the wood-stove club does not want you to join!

Then there are other deterring persons. These I dub the g.g.'s – government ghouls. Should you wish to do anything, their instant reaction is that you can't. If they dig deep enough they will find a law somewhere that says so.

The application of this principle to wood-stove installation arises in the Clean Air Act. I have already mentioned the implicit bias against wood burning present in the Act, but it must be dealt with more fully here because some over-enthusiastic wood-stove salespersons make the case that the offence lies in making smoke and not in burning an unauthorised smokeless fuel in a smoke control area.

This is not strictly true. At least, it is a more prudent course for you to assume that it is not strictly true.

The difficulty of giving a straight answer to a straight question is that the Clean Air Act is not, in fact, a single Act, but a large number of legislative instruments going under various names. The principle effect of these is to empower local authorities to make Smoke Control Orders for their districts. Embodied in these are a large number of detailed exemptions. Even the base legislation itself is confusing. For example, it is an offence for an occupier of premises to allow smoke emission from a chimney, unless the smoke is caused by the use of an authorised 'smokeless' fuel. It seems, therefore, that if a 'smokeless' fuel makes smoke, that is all right, but, if you burn an unauthorised fuel and it does not make smoke, you are committing an offence all the same. However, one of the provisions of the 1968 Act is that it is now an offence 'to acquire or to sell by retail for delivery in a Smoke Control Area any fuel other than an authorised fuel'.

For some time it has also been argued in the wood-stove trade that if one installed in a Smoke Control Area a stove that was capable of burning smokeless fuel as well as wood – and that burning the wood did not make smoke – this was permissible. This opinion seems to have arisen from a limited number of such installations that the authorities either do not know about, or have turned a convenient blind eye to. If it were offically challenged, I doubt there would be a good defence in law.

A limited number of wood-burning appliances have been passed for smokeless operation. These are certain kinds of domestic fireplaces, burning what is dubbed 'wood waste in clean condition' or 'clean wood waste of a size within the limits referred to in the manufacturer's instructions'. This latter stipulation applies to a wood-chip fired air heater. A German unit has also received the DOE's gold seal of approval so long as it only burns 'clean wood waste containing not more than 5 per cent sander dust and not more than 1 per cent plastic contamination'. Both of these wood-chip appliances are intended for industrial use. No domestic user would, in any case, be able to lay his hands easily on such a precisely defined fuel.

So far as ordinary wood-stove burning in private homes is concerned a letter recently received from the DOE wraps it up.

> So far, no wood-burning stove for domestic use has been exempted, and our information is that these stoves are unlikely to qualify. . . . Tests have been carried out to assess the position of wood as an air pollutant. Results showed that wood is two or three times smokier than any fuel so far authorised. It seems unlikely, therefore, that the burning of wood in a smoke control area will be permitted in the foreseeable future.

Some control area denizens are, for the present, permanently debarred from joining the wood-stove club.

There are other disqualifications that arise more from the commonsense of experience rather than government prohibition.

In the bad days of the 'fifties I lived in a London flat that occupied the top three floors of a six-storey Victorian terraced house. There were nine steps up from the street pavement to the entrance lobby, and another 121 steps to my flat. Heating was by coal in a massive open-throat fireplace. The living room measured 35 feet by 22 feet, and was 12 feet high. To heat this mausoleum in the winter it was necessary to let the fire blaze at full blast, which was about all it would do anyway.

Coal was stored on a roof garden at first-floor level, 83 steps down. To get coal delivered it was necessary for me to vanish from my office, hurtle across to the flat, bribe the coalmen that they would not risk a hernia when they clambered up from the street with a hundredweight at a time. That accomplished, I had to transport the coal the remaining distance up to the fireplace in a 30-pound brass coal bucket. Coal consumption was about a ton every month – about 90 pounds of coal each evening – three trips down and up again.

Wood has half the calorific value of coal. You must burn twice the quantity to generate the same heat. Imagine six trips a night! Even with the efficiency of the modern airtight stove, three to four hoistings of wood would have been necessary. Honestly, wood burning for city flat-dwellers is not practical. Consider yourself eliminated from the club. Even should your town house have a garden of some kind with reasonable access and you are not within the limits of smoke control legislation, I would still advise against wood stove installation. There are two other reasons.

First, where would you store the stuff? The traditional measure for wood is the cord. This is a volume of stacked logs – so called cord wood – eight feet long, four feet wide, four feet high – 128 cubic feet. At a reasonable estimate you would need about five cords of wood to see you through a year. Say, something in the region of 700 cubic feet – five cords and a bit over. That's not so bad, you will point out. A volume ten feet by ten feet by seven feet high – something less than a small garage.

But, that is not all. The purpose of stacking logs in cords, apart from the convenience of being able to measure them, is so that the wood will air dry. Wood freshly cut from the living tree needs least six months of air drying before it is fit to burn. The sap needs to be driven from it – another reason for cutting the wood into cord lengths, is to allow the air to get at it. You will also need to be able to get at the wood, section by stored section. So that, in practice, your wood will be stored in single line columns with a corridor between them. The storage space you will need must be increased by that amount.

All right, you come back at me, I don't need to take delivery of, and store, an entire year's supply in one go. As with coal, I can take in as much as it is convenient to do at any one time.

But that is exactly what you cannot do. There is no national delivery and supply service for wood as there is for coal. Wood is cut more particularly in the winter when the wood is not growing, and when fellers or farm labourers are not busy doing other things. If you are in the wood-fuel market and someone offers you the delivery of a year's supply, you grab it. You do not know when and where the next one will come from.

There are those who innocently suppose that, wood being a fairly solid fuel, its interests are watched over by the Solid Fuel Advisory Service, which sounds impartial, but isn't. The SFAS is funded by the Coal Board and coal is what they are there to push as a fuel. For the most part wood is something they try to pretend does not exist. It is true that in some offices they will grudgingly disgorge leaflets and information if pressed. But on the whole they are not about to divert traffic into the pockets of those they see as their rivals in the domestic fuel market.*

The most likely event is that if you live in a city or town – even if there is no smoke control legislation to stop you – there will be no supply of wood available to you. If you are enthusiastic, you may even consider making forays into the countryside yourself to bring back your wood fuel. I can only comment there that experience shows that the most likely outcome is that you will spend more on petrol, finding and transporting the wood, than you will save by burning it. If you are a town dweller, either high born or lowly, it is much better that you resign yourself to the reality that membership of the exclusive wood-stove club is not for you.

Edging gingerly sideways out of the city heartlands we move towards the halfway house of suburbia, something between

*This is now changing: the SFAS is getting interested in wood.

dispersed townland and concentrated countryside, yet having the characteristics of neither. This is a difficult area to assess for wood-stove use.

It is not likely that there will be smoke control legislation in operation. Most homes will have reasonable access to some kind of garden. It is even possible that garages are large enough to house one car and a wood supply instead of the second family car. Tree fellers or farms with available trees could be within convenient reach.

The recommendation whether to wood burn or not in such a home would, it seems to me, rest finally on two bases. It could be assumed that other factors being favourable adequate wood storage can be arranged in such a household. The more vital question is, could a wood supply be organised?

The first investigation might be a quick finger walk through your Yellow Pages. Turn to the listings under Wood: Carvers, Turners and Workers. All of these are likely to have scrap wood for sale. Much of this consists of slivers, splendid for kindling a fire to light, but not for continuous burning. Unless, that is, you want to sit by the fire acting as a one person non-stop conveyor belt. Such scraps, in the heat of a blaze, vanish in a couple of flame bursts. You need something rather more substantial.

If these sources are not satisfactory, find the Timber listings: Agents and Brokers (including Plywood Manufacturers), Timber Buildings (Building Contractors, Sectional and Portable Buildings), Timber Engineers, Timber Haulage Contractors, Importers and Merchants. Don't forget Furniture Makers. Somewhere in that lot you might well find wood going to waste.

What kind of a deal you might make, I cannot predict. Certainly, there will already be some way of clearing this waste from the producing premises. Possibly your negotiation will take place with the removers. But somewhere there you should find somebody who will deliver to you at a price, or let you come and collect at a lower price.

Tree Work Contractors are useful people to contact, not only because they have wood but because scrap-wood is a byproduct of their main work. It is a means of earning a little bit extra. If the firm is not interested in dealing with you, most likely one of their men will come to a personal arrangement with you on a personal cash basis. It is surprising how often wood turns up on a Sunday morning – just before the pubs open!

The autumn is a good time to tour farm districts to spy out those with copses of trees. Drop by the farmhouse and ask the farmer what he plans to do with them. Winter is the time when farm workers have time on their hands – time for a little productive tree management.

There are two methods. The tree can be coppiced, cut down to anything from ground level to chest height. If the tree is a conifer, this will probably kill it. If it is deciduous, new growth will come from the cut stump. Not always, but most leaf-dropping trees will coppice and most non-leaf dropping trees will not. The second method is to pollard the tree, to cut the branches back from the main stem above the height reached by browsing animals. Again, the tree does not die. It continues growing.

Both these methods produce quantities of small wood very suitable for burning in a modern wood stove. It may be that you can come to an arrangement with a farmer to take all his small wood – the main trunk or bole he can sell more profitably for industrial use. A single farm could easily satisfy your annual requirements. Oak produces a tonne of new timber per acre each year. Any farm with five acres of trees could supply you. You may have to go and scrabble about picking up the small wood yourself, making up estate car loads. This is a small price to pay.

Having secured supplies of wood and found somewhere to store them, that is far from being the end of the matter.

Alert and attentive readers will have noted an uneasy relationship between cords and tonnes of wood. I need to dig a little more deeply into this quantitative mire, if only for the purpose of being able to define the storage problem.

One day you will be bounding along a country lane in your family transport and you hear the nagging screech of the chain saw. Tracking it to source you find a trio of jolly tree fellers busy at their felling. Adopting one of your most winning smiles you

31

make overtures, enquiring into the possibility that you might share in their amplitude of wood waste.

One of them will quote you a price per tonne delivered. He might even, in his simple country fashion, still be thinking of a price per ton. No matter. What arrives on your doorstep in practice is a quantity of wood whose price is calculated in the tree person's mind as a price *per load*. This load is a flexible beast. It may mean the quantity of wood needed to fill his tractor trailer level to the side boards, or heaped as high as the springs will allow. Or somewhere between these two if it came on to rain just as they were in the middle of loading up. Or, if the field of trees they were felling did not produce quite as much small wood as they had estimated. Or, if another chap like yourself came asking for wood on the same afternoon. All these factors will influence the size of the loads delivered for which you have been quoted.

None of those remarks should be taken as intimating that tree fellers are devious or untrustworthy chaps. Just that their outlook is different. A lifetime of association with living and growing things accustoms them to adopt variable standards, adjustable between nature's bounty and nature's famine.

Let us go back to your primary negotiation. You want a fair price quoted for the wood you need. Note that phrase – the wood you need. If the wood is newly cut – green wood – you must air-dry it for at least six months before burning. That affects the price.

Will you accept the wood as it is, or do you require it in particular sizes? If you must have – let us imagine – logs no more than 40 centimetres long (say 16 inches) and 12 centimetres in diameter (say 5 inches), this must raise the price to you because the fellers must trim the wood before they make their delivery.

Also, whether the wood is hard wood (like oak) or soft wood (like conifer) will affect the price. Hard wood usually burns longer than soft wood and thereby commands a higher price (although it has a lower calorific value).

However, the point is, that eventually, on a Sunday morning or whenever, these feller fellows will turn up on your doorstep with wood for which they require payment. How do you cope? If you have ordered five tonnes, one of the chaps will undoubtedly assure you that the quantity being hawked at your door is 'five good loads'. Is it, though? Take a tape measure and roughly rule the length, depth and height of the pile as it lies on the trailer. How many cubic feet does it scale out to? Your assessment will be rough, but you should be able to come to some idea, adding on something for the domed heap at the centre of the pile, deducting something for the rounded corners. At 128 cubic feet to the cord, how many cords does the load come to? Having reached that figure, you must allow something else. If the wood is neatly stacked in measured lengths, as you ordered, you should deduct about a third from your figure – this being the air space between the wood. If the logs are loosely tumbled anyhow, you may have to deduct half for the air space factor.

Finally, you arrive at a true volumetric figure. And you ordered tonnes. Hard wood, such as oak, weighs somewhere between 50 and 55 pounds to the cubic foot, depending how dry it is. With the airspace allowances, this scales at between $1\frac{1}{4}$ and $2\frac{1}{4}$ tonnes per cord. Work to about $1\frac{1}{2}$ or $1\frac{3}{4}$ tonnes, depending on the size, quality and condition of the wood, and you can arrive at a figure that will satisfy the tree men. Oddly, this long-winded calculation will not make them testy. Rather, they respect the diligence of someone concerned to get it right, and pay fairly.

However, even that is not the point of my extended diversion. Because, what we now have is a large and well-defined load of logs at your door. It is the moment of truth. Can your house take it in?

If your suburban house is of such a design that there is no way through from front to rear other than through the house itself, then dispose of the logs as best you can and opt out of the wood-stove club. Rather you should use up expensive and increasingly scarce fossil fuel than you should pollute your life with unnecessary labour, and the interior of your house with twigs, wood droppings and crawlies. Just because wood has been cut, don't imagine that all its inhabitants have departed for other homes. Many of them have remained where they are, still comfortable and undisturbed by their nest's change of location. In carting wood through your home, some will drop off and find new accommodation.

Then, you must consider that condition specific to any suburb – the awkward neighbour syndrome. If, in your innocence, you believe that it will be quite acceptable for you to pile wood logs in your front garden – because it is not convenient for you to shift them through to the back – sooner or later someone will complain. If local authorities can prevent you from parking a caravan in your front garden, you can rest assured that a wood pile is equally preventable. I cannot quote you the legislation. That doesn't matter. You can be sure it exists.

Very well, you agree. And being the best kind of neighbour, you get all your wood round to the rear of your house, and even into your garage.

Does any part of your wood store, either out in the open or enclosed in your garage, lie adjacent to any part of the structure of your neighbour's messuage? If he is of the awkward cast, the complaint will be levelled at your back door that wood worm, beetle, or wet or dry rot is penetrating from your wood through the separating fence into some part of his domain.

If you surmount these hurdles, there are others. Let us suppose further that in the pursuit of long-lasting health and happiness – and as an alternative to soulless and pointless jogging – you elect to chop and saw your wood logs into the size your stove will accept. You will be astonished how much muck will accumulate in six months of this daily exercise. As your waist line shrinks, the piles of saw dust, discarded twiglets and cut ends will rise, like an incoming tide, around your ankles. You always intended to clear up each day as you cut, but you don't. And these woody remnants, you will be told, harbour all manner of unwanted life forms from rodents to infestatious insects. Away with it, and away with you and your confounded wood stove.

Reluctantly, as one weighs the balance, there is a strong predilection towards eliminating suburban households from

34

Lange Hamlet

Mørso Horatio

the wood-stove club. If you are very keen, there is a chance for you. If there are special circumstances . . . only you can decide. My purpose in raising these objections to you joining the club is to avert heartache and regret for misguided decisions. Much sales effort is being put into the promotion of wood stoves. Glossy brochures with glamorous pictures abound. Don't be taken in. In the nicest and most legitimate of ways, these sales approaches are cons.

About five years ago when the wood-burning idea began to get under way in the UK, one of the first companies in the field adopted the tactic of asking all its first customers whether they would become agents. The reasoning ran on these lines: wood stoves are best sold to persons living in the country. The customers to whom they made advances all did so. Having bought a stove of their own, each would have at least a demonstrator on the premises with which to impress prospective clients. The reasoning has proved sound. The firm, and one presumes their home-based agents, prospers.

On the whole, then, country dwelling persons are those for whom the wood stove club is best able to cater. Of course, I accept that my previous definitions of home environment were entirely arbitrary. No doubt there are compact townships close to woodland where wood stoves would burn well. Equally, I can think of bleak, cheerless, treeless country districts where wood would be the last fuel one could heat with.

To burn wood one needs space. I don't mean a large house. The smallest cottages burn wood. It is their natural fuel. In every country district two or three clumps of wood smouldering in a grate have traditionally been the direct path to warmth. The wood comes from neighbouring trees, owned by the cottage dweller, or by arrangement with the land owner, often arising from ancient custom. Farm workers burn wood because the fuel is just lying or growing about their place of work waiting to be picked up. It costs nothing.

Newly built country homes burn wood for much the same reasons. In their locality there is a source of wood that can be cut into. For these home owners the modern glossy brochures mean something. Standing in the corner of their up-to-the-minute labour-saving establishment is a vast cast-iron streamlined wood stove. Often bought for appearance and not necessarily the best one for the job, but burning cheap or free wood just the same.

The vast rambling Victorian monster residences that a decade ago were all scrambling aboard the oil- or gas-fired central heating bandwagon are now busily scrambling back to wood as their owners gloomily contemplate mounting fuel bills.

Let me quote some figures culled from researches published by the Consumers' Association. They are the costs for heating an ordinary home by various means. For these calculations to be on a standardised basis, it is assumed that the annual rate of consumption is 16,000 useful kilowatt hours (kWh). Going back to 1976, the cost for that level of heating by electricity was £200. Oil heating would have cost you £150, coal about £120 and gas somewhere in the region of £110. In each case, I have taken the top rate applicable.

Coming forward a year to 1977, we find that electrical heating, still on the basis of 16,000kWh per annum, has gone up to £230. Oil has risen to £190, gas to £140 and coal to £130.

Another year passes and we begin to see the dramatic impact of inflation on fuel prices. By 1978, our standard, calculated electricity bill has shot up to £450, oil to £330, gas is costing £230 and coal £180.

As I write, increases in coal prices have already been agreed for the winter of 1979–80, 8 per cent increases are pending for gas and electricity, and the OPEC nations have just raised the global price of crude oil by just under 9 per cent, with surcharges of anything up to 25 per cent on top of that.

In the country, wood prices are not as standardised as those of the industrial heartland I have quoted, but a rude scale runs like this – rough wood delivered in an 'as is' condition costs from £8 to £10 per tonne. Assuming the same 16,000kWh per annum, five of such tonnes would be consumed in the year. If the wood is cut to small sizes the price goes up to between £12 and £15 per tonne, depending on the labour involved. If a local farmer is felling, or having felled, a few of his trees, he may agree to allow you to come and gather the small wood yourself. He charges you nothing because you are doing him a favour. If he plans to sow crops, or graze animals the wood pieces would have to be cleared first before he can do so. This is a wood source available only to country persons.

There is another. Wherever there are Forestry Commission forests and woodlands, the possibility exists of securing from them an annual licence to pick up dead wood. This, of course, has to be under the control of their foresters, who will direct you where and when you can gather, but it costs only a pound or so a year and is available only to *genuine full-time local residents*. You cannot zoom down from the city, or establish yourself in a holiday home and claim a licence. You are disqualified once again.

In the country, all the strings of the wood-burning pattern are pulled together to form a firm weave. Supplies of fuel are all about you at low cost, or no cost. Even the smallest country cott will have space enough to take in, saw, chop and store wood. The wood ash that comes from the fire nourishes the vegetable patch. The wisps of smoke that rise from your chimney do not pollute the atmosphere, nor will any of your neighbours find themselves in disagreement with what you are doing. They are most likely doing the same themselves.

This is where the wood-stove club offers its members the greatest benefits, and, harshly realistic though my assessment may be, it is fully in line with the proposition I advanced in The Introduction that, at best, one could look towards wood fuel, in this country, to satisfy about 5 per cent of the domestic fuel market.

2
WILL WOOD HEAT YOUR HOME?

We are still trying to ease you through the stiff portals of the exclusive wood-stove club. The membership committee has vetted the district where you live. It has confirmed to its own satisfaction that supplies of wood are available to you, that you have space to store the stuff, time and energy to saw and chop it, and that no other impediments exist to your wood heated joys and hopes. Yet, still it doesn't give you the full thumbs up. What, you want to know, your gorge rising, does it want now?

What it wants is to inspect your premises to confirm that they are suited to wood heat. Of course, you will think that your house is as good as any other in that regard. But, I do assure you that this is not necessarily so.

If it should happen that you live in a replica of a traditional New England house (or, if you live in one of the New England states, you are housed in the genuine article), the immediate nod of approval would be beamed your way. Membership of the wood-stove gang is definitely for you. Such dwellings are entirely suitable for this exercise. To begin with they will certainly have a capacious cellar; the internal layout will be of the open-plan style; and, being built of stout baulks of wood, the walls and roof will be excellent insulators.

The proper place for a wood stove, as New England house owners know, is down in the cellar. In the floor above it one ensures there is some kind of slit or slot. Warm air from the stove rises through this and follows its nose to every last nook and cranny in the place. Not until it has fully done this job will the timbers of the walls and roof permit it to escape.

Traditional New England households have been leading this well-warmed winter life for upwards of three centuries, and it

40

suits them very well. The rest of us must make shift with the next best we can arrange. Even if we have cellars, the vital slits or slots will be missing, as will the open-plan arrangement.

To get the best of whatever compromises we can devise, the principle of the activity must be grasped, the essential element of which is that, for the maximum benefit, heat from any source must be circulated and contained. Obvious, you will argue, surely, that must be the basis for all central-heating systems. Well, yes, in a sense. But in homes made up of numbers of individual boxes or rooms, there is a tendency to think of warming each one at a time. It is to us Old Englanders as traditional as the whole house idea of the new chaps across the water.

Perhaps because of this we have never come to terms with hot-air heat. I have lived with this in California – the fuel being natural gas – and I have stayed in homes warmed by oil-fuelled air. They work well, even though they offend against my 'unseen fire' theory. There are gas- and oil-fired hot-air systems available in the United Kingdom. Somehow, they don't seem to fire one's enthusiasm here as well as in America. The climate of opinion must be against them.

However, they do point us in the direction of circulated warmth, which must be the starting place for every home-heat plan, wood warmed or whatever. Of course, the wood stove could be shoved in anywhere, a match put to it and, when the flames blaze, all the doors could be left open. That could be done, but it wouldn't do. If there is one concept of the traditional British house that prevails, it is draughts, icy blasts that attack the nether regions and all points north.

Where shall the stove be placed? An odd question you will think. Stoves are placed in hearths. So they are. But wood stoves are often of the free-standing, self-contained style. Within limits they can go anywhere. The limits we will examine shortly. For the moment, let us keep our options open.

In an old Devonian house I visited recently, a wood stove had been installed at the base of the staircase well that rose up through the centre of the structure. Warm air billowed up and was wafted into the rooms opening from it on each floor. Most effective. It might have been even more so if the thick outer walls had been composed of something other than brick. Even the driest brick is porous and holds residual moisture. This cuts down its insulating qualities. Valuable heat gets out before it should.

I live in a slate house – walls 2 feet thick, horizontally layered with flat slabs of grey slate. Elsewhere in my locality, old farm houses and the like are built of granite and other stone. All are capable of insulating like billy-oh. Which means the walls hold heat. No need to pour out money in heat store units. Get the walls warm and they stay warm, no matter what is freezing the cockles of the outside world.

If you begin to look at your house with these ideas in mind you will be able to judge whether heat will move freely about your premises. And, when generated, if that heat will be held in.

Let us be generous for the moment and assume you pass muster on insulation. Some alternative, however, has to be found to knocking down your inside walls. Air trunks could be pushed through with vents for the hot air to escape. Or, micro-bore copper pipes can be threaded from one room to another and connected to efficient radiators, double-layered, to provide the maximum of surface from which the heat can surge into your house air.

With the flexibility that this offers, we now return to the central question – where do you put your stove? To some degree the answer is conditioned by what kind of stove you are choosing to put in. I will be coming to detail comments of that kind in Chapter 4. For the moment I will restrict myself to remarks applicable to any heating unit.

Much depends on your life style as well as your home. Do you live in your kitchen? Does the stove have to compete with the telly for attention and interest? Is the sink, with all its awesome potential for washing-up, as much a feature as the padded horse hair armchairs by the fire? If so, then you may wish to work your wood stove to a non-stop schedule.

I make that point because you have the option. Wood is not like any form of solid fuel – the modern euphemism for coal and its by-products. Coal is a slow responder. You have to work hard to get it alight. If you choose to burn it slowly you cannot rapidly change to any other mode. Having for some time burnt it fiercely, you cannot, at the flick of a finger, slow it down.

You can with wood. It is quickly responsive in a way that coal is not. Your stove can be held down to the merest glimmer all night. When you return to life in the morning, the simple act of opening the damper is generally enough to provoke an instant flame. At the other end of the day, the brisk burning that has kept the family mopping its brows through the evening can be lowered with matching speed to an all-night glow by pulling down the fire's shutters.

And if the sweep of these comments should seem to imply a leaning towards larger, older houses as suitable for wood heat, let me dispel that at once. I know of many small, modern country bungalow-type places where wood warmth is enjoyed to the full.

Something else has to be nudged out of the road towards wood enjoyment. I don't know whether this arises from TV dramas where log fires are simulated by two feeble gas flickers fondling plastic logs. But, common experience of wood-heated pubs and homes has conditioned me to a wide-spread concept of a wood fire as two chunky wood lumps leaning wretchedly against each other corner to corner from whence arises a thin flame and matching dim glow.

A proper wood fire has a majesty and a roar, it is a lion among fires. This should never be forgotten. If your fire ever lacks the capacity for roaring then it must be too old, too senile and starved of essential nutrients. Indeed, this get-up-and-roar quality of wood firing is a very good starting place to discover what wood burning is all about and just exactly what it may, or may not, do for you.

We return to the question of where your stove should be, and what freedom you have to choose, and within what limits. The first criterion is practical. Your wood smoke and residual heat must go up a chimney. This is not only to let it get away and not make a nuisance of itself, but also to create the vital draught that roars through your fire and makes it burn. This roaring is just warm air passing through a narrow opening causing a local disturbance there.

If you live in an old house it is likely you have no problem. It may be you have surplus chimneys, old ones bricked up, and even some you don't know about. With the modern type of free-standing stove, virtually the only structural work necessary to make your apparatus operable is to cut a small hole through the room wall into the chimney chamber, connect your stove pipe to it, and you are in the wood-heat business. Theoretically, your internal stove pipe could run right across the room before entering the flue. This would give you the choice of placing your stove in the remotest corner, if that is what you want. But this is not to be recommended – not if you wish to avoid tar.

To this point I have talked only of room heating. It may be that other considerations are also vital. I must be able to see the fire that is warming me. That cuts down my range of choice where the stove is put. You may want your wood heat to cook as well as warm you, and this narrows your choice of position.

More importantly, and here we slide into some deepish waters, there are Building Regulations. These can be inspected, if you are resolute, at most public libraries. What is more useful is a compact guide to these Regulations put out by the Architectural Press in annual editions. Again, consult your local library. If you are a wood-fire DIY person then you will have to live with Building Regulations as your bible, if you don't already do so. Arranging for one of your local handy persons to do the installation allows you to breathe down someone else's neck. Contracting with a builder swells the cost but shoots the ball into their court.

The main structural requirements are straightforward enough. Anything related to your wood stove – chimney, flue pipe, hearth and fireplace if you have them – must be built of unburnable material. As you are hardly likely to arrange otherwise there is no need for us to linger there.

Neither must it be possible for combustion products to escape into the building. This is not so obvious. Often, in an old house, the chimney from one hearth joins with that from another fireplace. In my own house, the dining-room chimney runs at an angle of 30° up across the wall and branches with that from one of the upstairs bedrooms at a point some 20 feet above ground level. When I connected my wood stove to the chimney in the downstairs room, it was necessary to seal off the branch to the bedroom. It would have still been possible to use that fireplace by fitting a separate flue, but I chose the easier option of closing the fireplace completely.

There are two reasons for this requirement. If one flue is joined by another, hot air rising in the first flue pulls in cold air from the second one. So that the vital draught which is going to keep your wood fire burning at its bushy brightest is whistling through an empty grate elsewhere, instead of through your burning area. And, if a back pressure occurs in the chimney flue – caused perhaps by a gust of wind – then the smoke and fumes from the fire will be blown back down the second flue, filling the room attached to it with nasty unbreathable muck.

Finally, by means of an air-tight trap door, or through the stove itself, it must be possible to pass through some kind of cleaning appliance to sweep the flue free of the by-products of burning. Normally, we associate the sweep and his brushes with this operation. But there is an older method that is returning to us from America, whence the early settlers took it. This might prove easier for you to do yourself than the sweep-brush technique. It supposes that you can get on your roof and to the chimney top. Down this you pass a small weight tied to a length of cord, twine or rope. Supposing that you know your chimneys and have chosen the right one, the weight will dangle down into your stove from where it can be pulled by your willing helper below into the room. You remove the weight – or rather, your helper does – and it is replaced by a small fir tree, say, three or four feet high. This is tied to the rope by its roots. When you hear the shout from below that all is ready, you pull it up through the flue. It bursts at last from the chimney top showering you with black bits. But your chimney is clear for another season's burning.

Another complex batch of regulations deals with the construction of fireplaces and hearths. These are much too detailed to cover fully here. But as I am primarily concerned

Sweeping a chimney: a small weight tied to a cord (a) is dropped down the chimney to the hearth (b); a small tree or bush is tied to the cord (c) and is pulled back to the roof top (d)

with wood stoves as complete self-contained units, I will restrict myself to requirements that apply to them.

A free-standing fire must stand on what is called a 'constructional hearth'. By this is meant a hearth made of non-combustible material to a minimum thickness of 50 millimetres (about 2 inches). There are other specifications about laying down air spaces between the stove and burnable surrounds. There must also be an adequate supply of combustion air for the fire to burn efficiently and to discharge into the chimney.

This brings me back, neatly I hope, to that roar. It is the heart of wood firing. If your fire roars, it has heart, and you need worry about it no more.

This question of roaring, of how much a fire should roar and in what manner, has taken up the time of thinkers in the wood-stove field for about the past two centuries. In this developmental thought, you will be astonished how the same ideas pop up, again and again, each time as if entirely new.

I shall have somewhat more to say about this when I get into the question of the stove itself. For the present, I am trying to get to grips with your house and what goes on inside it. To that degree, I must offer some explanation of what happens in the fire, and how best you can further the process.

We have already been through the chemical formula for burning in the Introduction. Wood sugar and cellulose are broken down to carbon dioxide and water by the intake of oxygen, which allows it to burn. This oxygen is delivered to the fire by an inrush of air. Obviously, if the fire is burning in one of the rooms in your house then that is where the air is coming from. Having had some of its oxygen extracted by the burning process and at the same time having been made hot, the air shoots away up the chimney. If this process goes on, then the natural expectation must be that your room will soon be empty of air. As, obviously, this does not happen, we have to conclude that more air is coming into the room from somewhere else in the house. And that from wherever that somewhere else is, more air is coming into the house from outside to top it up. Luckily, it is pretty hard to build an airtight house, the stuff gets in somehow. If you do double-seal all your windows and doors, then some provision will have to be made for air to come into the house in a controlled way – through vents of some kind – to satisfy the demands of the fire.

If you are building a house, or remodelling to the point where planning permission is necessary, then Building Regulations solve the problem. Wherever there is an open fire, there must be a ventilated opening to the outside air. With any other type of installation there must be a permanent vent to the exterior with a minimum unobstructed area at least equal to the area of the flue connection, or – and here the builder's bible waxes technical: '550 square millimetres for each kilowatt (or part thereof) of maximum output, whichever is the greater. If there

Hot – but stuffy

Warm and fresh – but watch those drafts

are two or more appliances in the room, the same rule applies.'
In other words, you just double up if there are two fires, and so
on, pro rata.

In case you enjoy playing these arithmetical games on your
domestic calculator, most wood stoves have their output quoted
in BThU's. About 3300 of these make up one kilowatt.

This operating principle is quite different to that of electric
fires or warm-air central heating. With those systems you can
double-glaze your windows, put draught-excluders round all
your doors and just keep on feeding the same old, warm stale air
round and round.

Burning fires are quite different. They must have air, and so a primary consideration in planning their installation is to make sure that enough of this is on tap. This is important.

What comes in – in this case – must go out. The exit is via the chimney. It is now germane to our investigation into your house's wood burning potential to discover what those Building Regulations have to say on the subject of chimneys. Their first stipulation is that the chimney be lined with an approved kind of lining. It is important to remember here that the Regulations are concerned with every kind of application, not just wood fires, so that when they list as meeting with official approval linings made of kiln burnt aggregate and high alumina cement, glazed clay pipes and similar substances, no acknowledgement is being made to the fact that these are unsuitable for wood fires.

Wood fires produce tar. You will remember that when I detailed the burning formula I mentioned that other substances were also involved. These are certain oils and resins present in the wood to a variable degree. This is quite a complicated issue and one that needs to be kept under firm control.

There are two extreme positions. Your wood fire may generate so much tar that every few weeks your chimney spontaneously bursts into flame and the neighbourhood Fire Brigade virtually keep a team of chaps constantly on the alert for fire on your premises. Or, your fire could generate almost no tar at all.

The average is likely. If you keep your flues reasonably swept, your fire burns well and the installation has been properly done, you will have no trouble.

Tar forms, in the first place, on the inside of the fire chamber or casing when you burn green wood – i.e., wood that is freshly cut and from which the natural sap has not been air-dried away. Tar also tends to form when the fire is burning at a low temperature. The air rising from it is warm rather than hot. Instead of shooting up the flue at speed it ambles up casually, losing heat and momentum all the way. Because it contains a quantity of water vapour from the burning process, this tends to condense on the flue pipe inner wall. When this happens, tar is

49

also deposited. Fires, then, that burn low all day and are kept in with an overnight glimmer will tend to tar up.

The two antidotes are, clearly, first, never to burn green wood, and second, to keep the fire raging at a good temperature. However, this is not necessary all the time. Even if your fire merely twinkles most of the day, so long as you fling wide the dampers and give it its head for at least half an hour each day, most of the tar previously deposited will be burned off.

I can illustrate this with practical demonstrations. In the house we have a large Danish Passat central-heating wood-burning boiler. It is built like a bed-sitting room, being a vast chamber nearly 6 feet long and 5 feet high. Almost anything flammable can be shoved into it – twigs, saw dust, tree trunks, kitchen waste, even bird droppings! It is surrounded by a capacious water jacket that supplies a substantial hot-water tank and some 22 radiators. This monster burns day and night at a slow flicker. Six months of unbroken burning this winter has layered the inside wall with black tar, crisped by heat, to a depth of about 1 centimetre (just under ½ inch).

In another part of the house a Belgian glass-fronted Kamina has been alight every day for the same period, but has not been kept in overnight. This has been run, deliberately, at very high temperatures. The room thermometer has often bubbled up to over 80°F, at which point connecting room doors are flung open to waft in additional draughts. The fire chamber in the Kamina is completely free of tar. Feeling upwards with the hand as far as the arm can reach discovers no trace of the muck.

This is because we ran to the expense of having the chimney lined throughout with double-wall insulated stainless-steel flue pipe. This is very expensive stuff, running currently at about £10 per foot and likely to increase shortly. In my view, it is an expense well worth bearing. Constricting the air flow accelerates its speed. By insulation the inner wall of the flue pipe retains its heat. Both of these influences have the effect of giving the rising hot air an extra urge to dash up to the exterior and take all its tatty tar with it.

Or rather, I tell a lie. When I say that we lined the chimney throughout with double-skinned, stainless-steel flue pipe, that was the intention. What stood in our way was something that may stand in your way also. A kink or sharp bend in the chimney. Short of a substantial demolition job, there did not seem to be a way round this.

Our solution was to take the liner up as high as it would go, and at that level to put in another flue door. The thinking goes like this: the hot emission from the fire down below comes zooming up to this height with no difficulty. If it is going to cool down, slow down, condense and deposit tar anywhere, it will be here where the flue liner stops. From this second trap up to the chimney top on the roof is only a matter of some 15 feet. A simple job to bung a flue brush up it, or haul an upended tree through it.

Since we installed our fires, a new Canadian process, shortly to be introduced to the UK, has solved the problem. The heart of the technique is a wide, pliable tube with perforated walls. This is inserted in the chimney round all the awkward bends. The end of the tube in the chimney is sealed. A sealing compound is forced around the tube. When this has set, the tube is deflated and withdrawn. This, apparently, seals the chimney as effectively as steel liners.

The day comes when your fire is fitted and working, what will then surprise you are its 'off' days. You get them and so do I. However, you don't expect fires to get them. Yet they do. No matter how wide you fling open the dampers: no matter how briskly you prod and re-arrange the logs, sticks and twigs, no matter how often you try to give the fire a bit of a boost with a paraffin fire lighter, it obstinately glimmers, flickers, fizzes and will not roar. Why?

There are all kinds of explanations. You have to feel a bit sorry for the chaps who design wood stoves. They are so often fumbling in the dark. There are so many variables they cannot predict. It is not at all like coal that, within narrow limits, is pretty much always the same kind of stuff. Design a stove to burn anthracite and you know where you are. You know its composition, state and size. You can go ahead and plan a stove to burn it and be confident of the results.

Not with wood. The poor designer does not know what type of wood will be burnt, what condition it will be in, what size it will be. On top of that he has no idea of the prevailing conditions when the fire is burning. As wood is a more responsive fuel than coal, it is more sensitive to atmospheric conditions. Low air pressure puts it off. Damp air puts a damper on it. A lack of wind depresses it. Low temperatures give it a chill. Wet wood acts like a wet blanket.

If this doesn't make the average wood fire sound as temperamental as a Callas, there is more. It doesn't like wind from the wrong direction. Of course, I can't tell you what the wrong direction is. Every fire has its own ideas about that. But you won't be long in finding out!

Your house does not exist in isolation. There are things all round it – other houses, buildings, trees, roof tops, even hillsides. When the wind comes from a certain direction and with enough strength, it bounces back from these to your chimney causing eddies, down draughts, back pressure. These stop the hot gases rising freely from the chimney into the atmosphere. If the hot gas can't make good speed, the flow of oxygen into the fire down below is impeded. So the fire burns less well.

The opposite also happens. On some days, it seems you have only to place a match somewhere in the general vicinity of your fire for it to take flame and roar away at you like a pride of lions, bulging with heat (assuming that is what lions bulge with). On these days, the wind is coming from some direction your fire happens to like. As it races past the chimney top it sucks the hot stuff out, pulling more oxygen through the fire, boosting your blaze.

Now these slings and arrows of outrageous burning are a touch inconvenient. You want to even things out. For an evening of comfort you don't want to shiver crouching round a reluctant stove, nor to be flung back from it by the heat. A steady and reviving flow of warmth is the ideal and to achieve this you try to average out the high and low spots in your wood stove's performance. You do this by fitting a cowl to the chimney pot. There are designs enough to satisfy every whim:

Assorted cowls

tapering shapes with intricate louvres right down to a simple inverted gutter. Unless your problem is acute, probably the simplest is the best. With one proviso. It does hamper your chimney sweeping. A cowl clamped across your chimney top will stop a flue brush coming up it. This isn't vital. Sweeps have a way of working the brush up as far as it will go, just below the cowl, and waggling it about to get rid of the muck they have cleared from inside the chimney flue. But, you'd have a tough time shoving even the smallest tree through.

It may be that your chimney won't need anything at all and will merrily belch away every day in the calendar. Lots do. I just raise the point in case yours is one of the sticky ones. The most sensitive are likely to be modern, thin-skinned chimneys. They lack substance. Old thick-walled chimneys of yesteryear have plenty of intestinal fortitude.

So, will your house do for wood heat, or not? To help you decide I have flung everything at you from Building Regulations upwards. Your head is still in a bit of a whirl. Let me clear it with a pretty straight from the shoulder description of how my own wood burning has worked out in practice. For simplicity, I will stick to the Kamina.

From the constructional hearth aspect, there was no difficulty choosing a place for it. The whole of the downstairs floor is concrete, thick enough to qualify under Building Regulations. We decided to put it in the corner of the room where the previous paraffin wick heater had been. From there we could put a stainless-steel flue up to the ceiling, angle it through the ceiling/floor into the wall above and lead it into the chimney chamber coming from the upstairs bedroom. The kink in the chimney prevented any further flue lining.

Downstairs, in what was to become our dining-room, a triangular plinth of concrete was built to fill the corner. In front of this, level with it, we placed a marble slab from an old wash stand. The Kamina stands on the concrete. The marble catches any ash droppings.

Having a naked flue pipe in the corner of one's room is not the most attractive feature. But, our house is built of solid slate. It stands on the site of an old Victorian slate quarry. Outside, pieces of slate, from slivers to slabs are just lying about waiting to be picked up. Whenever I dig the garden, great plates of it come up.

Pick it up is what we did, using the material to build a splendid fireplace tapering from the Kamina stove top up to the ceiling. Beneath this is concealed the flue pipe. The structure also acts as a heat store holding warmth for up to two days.

With the position of the stove decided, our next unravelling was how to distribute the heat from it. Things have been made much easier now than they were when we installed the Kamina. For us, after a good deal of ferreting about, the solution turned out to be a rather primitive back boiler – one of the first to be introduced into a wood stove here, and somewhat basic in conception. For which there is an immediate explanation. A substantial proportion of the wood stoves sold in Britain are imported from Europe where the wood-burning tradition has never been broken as it has been here. The Europeans, however, being more used to wood stoves and their characteristics, are generally content to burn them as closed units with the heat being radiated from the solid cast-iron casing. The British concept of house warmth (because of the way the houses are constructed) is central heating achieved by circulating hot water through radiators. The UK importers of the European stoves moved quickly to respond to this market need by introducing hastily made back boilers that were fabricated here. As evidence of the lack of forethought, I can evidence our own experience. Our Belgian Kamina stove features a barbecue grill that is mounted on a vertical support in the fire and swings into position above the burning logs when you want to cook on it. However, when the British made back boiler was bolted in place at the back of the fire chamber there was no longer any room for the grill. On later models, this has now been remedied with a boiler that fits in a higher position and is angled across the top of the fire.

Another penalty has now come to light. During the summer we have swept all our chimney flues. Because of the badly placed back boiler in our Kamina stove, it is no longer possible to unscrew and lower the baffle in the roof of the fire chamber (see page 77). As a result, the short length of flue pipe that connects the stove to the chimney cannot be swept. We have to take on trust the theory that the uprise of hot air from the fire will keep it clear.

Two British manufacturers – Woodwarm of Cullompton in Devon, and Logfires of Devizes in Wiltshire – have avoided this difficulty by using wrap-around water jackets in their fire chambers.

The back boiler in question consists of a flat metal water container. Two pipes, carried through the stove casing (we had to cut the holes for those, also!), bring water in at the bottom and take it out at the top. The hot water is fed up to the hot-water tank, from whence a small electric pump pushes the warming fluid out to six radiators. If the electricity fails the system will still work by convection, but not as well.

Deliberately, we fitted more radiators than the manufacturer's brochure advised. We wanted to test the fire to its limit. The recommendation was for three. We put in six. And indeed, the fire will heat six. But not to sizzling heat. A good, steady, hot-to-the-hand warmth is what results. Enough to keep the chill from the house in the worst weather. Cut down to four and the fire will sizzle these in no time. Depending on the day, the time of day and external conditions, you can play games experimenting which radiators shall be switched off.

One other house matter must be raised. I shall be getting into the firewood area in Chapter 4. But a part of it is a house issue. Our main wood supply is kept outside under the car port. But you don't want – at least, I don't! – to keep charging outdoors in the dark of night to lug in wood logs. A three-day supply is kept inside the house in a large, flat-topped wood chest that doubles as a seat. Supplies are taken from this to whichever of the fires is in use, which for our present purposes is the Kamina. Each day I bring more wood in from the car port to keep up the supply. And I drag more logs in from the woods and saw them under the car port to keep that end of the wood chain going.

From the first it was clear that the overall problem in running the fire was, not a shortage of heat, but rather the opposite. Too much of it. Some nights it has you gasping. With anything like decent wood it bursts into life very easily. The water pump is switched on and as much heat as the back boiler can soak up is sent round to the radiators. A considerable surplus remains.

But that is with decent wood. Because we took over the house last autumn and knew nothing of the niceties of wood husbandry, we entered the dark tunnel of winter with no stocks of wood prepared. It was necessary to trudge to the woods each day, even when the ground was several feet deep in snow, to drag in dead or fallen wood. This had to be cut to a size that fitted the Kamina stove chamber – about 40 centimetres long with a maximum diameter of about 12 centimetres.

The result was that one often faced the task of running the stove with just a pile of sodden wood. This takes some doing. I am not going to deal with lighting techniques here and so we can assume for the moment that the fire is feebly alight and somehow we have to keep it going. No good trying to struggle with wet wood. It won't work.

The solution is to pile it on top of the stove casing. (Some desperate souls have been known to start their fires by drying wood in the gas oven!) As the casing warms – and when the fire is blazing it is too hot to touch – the moisture is driven off as vapour to the point where the wood is sufficiently 'undamped', if there is such a word, that it will burn. I say undamped because such wood never gets totally dry and you can always feel a residue of moisture in it.

So there you are, the fire working, making ground against the cold, even with damp wood, and the next load is drying out.

Suddenly, the unexpected happens. Flames burst up from the wet logs, and you begin to understand why wood is described as a responsive fuel. When the casing gets hot enough, any wood drying on top of it will ignite spontaneously. So watch it!

This brings me to the final point. Where to place the wood box inside the house. Even with the best wood, bits drop off. If the wood box is well away from the outside door then the route to it will be littered with droppings. Some of these will get up and walk away. Just because a piece of wood is dead or damp, or both, and has been lying under the car port for some time, and has then spent further days inside the wood box does not mean that all its natural inhabitants have left it. On the contrary, some of them may have concluded that the move was a change for the better. It is important, therefore, to keep the wood box as near to the door as possible, and equally close to the fire. When you look at the interior of your house, solving that equation may take some doing. A wood box that is near the door may automatically be far away from the fire. Move it near the fire and it is a long way back to the door. Think about it.

If none of this deters you – the membership committee votes in favour of both your neighbourhood and your house – then we can assume you are going ahead with joining the wood-stove club and start talking about lighting your first fire.

3

INSIDE THE STOVE

You've at last sparked your way into the wood burners' enclave and still your perplexities are not ended. You feel yourself to be on the brink of something big – a Grand Canyon of torrefaction, a Himalaya of calefaction. But, no one is prepared to draw you a guide line. Wood-burning club members, you argue, should surely be bona fide owners and operators of genuine wood-burning appliances. Wood stoves don't grow on trees, you discover. They are often thinner on the ground than snow in a heat wave.

Never mind – you are an enthusiast, you persist, stumbling through the fog of not knowing. Until suddenly, you trip across a clutch of them in a remote countryside establishment. The dearth becomes a glut. Stoves of every kind, shape, style and disposition abound. Their mute fire doors seem bent on catching your eye.

A choice has to be made. Sales leaflets are thrust into your uncertain hands. You read them, words like 'traditional quality' and 'advanced technology' flicker across your critical faculties. You sense yourself being driven towards a decision.

What is urgently needed, you conclude, is some wood-burning Sherlock Holmes to unravel these pyrogenic confusions. And, here am I, ready and willing to give you the benefit of a vast experience of trial and error. Mostly, the latter.

What is going on inside the wood stove, anyway? A very good question, and to answer it we must go back to the origins of the wood stove, to that American man of many parts, Benjamin Franklin (1706–90), who, when he wasn't flying kites in thunderstorms, making experiments to find the potency of cider and acting as an adviser to the newly formed revolutionary government in France, was also turning his mind to the problem of heating one's home with wood.

He noted that in the German farmhouses of his native Philadelphia, too much hot air escaped up the chimney. Its rapid exit pulled in cold air to replace it, so that persons seated in the room had tanned faces if they could get close enough to the fire, and chilly, draught-fanned backs. To cut this down, Franklin designed a sliding door to limit air flow between the fire and chimney flue.

From which he discovered something interesting. Rooms in which this device was fitted became chokingly stuffy. What was happening now, was that not enough hot air was going up the chimney. The surplus was wafting round and round the farm house rooms, keeping the place warm right enough, but stopping any fresh air from entering.

Franklin saw that a compromise was needed. The old open fire sent too much heat up the chimney: his damped fire did not send enough. To find his way towards a middle performance he came up with the idea of a free-standing fireplace. This was a cunning appliance that I must describe in some detail, because pretty well all subsequent wood stove thinking is based on it; but first we must also have a look at his conclusions about the actual wood-burning process. According to his observations, there are three phases. First, most of the water in the wood must be vapourised. Freshly cut green wood has up to 50 per cent of moisture. A year's air drying will reduce this to about 20 per cent. Quality furniture makers like to work with kiln-dried wood. Even after several hours in a hot, dry oven, the wood still holds about 8 per cent of water. When you light an open fire you can see this happening. Clouds of what looks like smoke, but mostly isn't, puff away up the flue. This goes on for a moment or so, then long, flickering tongues of yellow flame lick out. Stage two has started: the volatiles have ignited. These are the natural oils and resins in the wood. They burn at a lower temperature than the fibrous matter of which wood is composed. If your fireplace is not efficient, these volatiles will not burn completely. They mix with what is left of the water vapour, and then you get a thickish smoke resulting. It is this mixture of volatile oil and moisture that creates the tar problem.

The final stage observed by Franklin is the burning of the wood itself, producing little smoke and not much in the way of a blaze – usually a small, hard, whitish flame pegging away at the base of the taller, willowy, yellow ones.

This is pretty accurate stuff, and about the only modification a modern wood-burning technician would wish to add is that, properly speaking, wood itself doesn't burn. When wood is heated its solid components turn to gas. As these gases burn they produce heat, which converts more of the solid wood into gas, and so on.

However, to revert to Franklin and his deliberations: he mulled over the conflict of interest between ventilated, chilly farmhouse rooms, and well-warmed stuffy ones, and solved it with the Pennsylvania fireplace.

This works by splitting the heating operation into two distinct sections. First, there is the fireplace in which a fire merrily roars. Rising up in the fireplace is an air chamber, which is sealed from the fire. The air chamber connects with the cellar beneath the room. Hot air and flame from the fire curls up around this air chamber, rising over the top, and then – because there is nowhere else to go – back down the far side. At the base of the air chamber, on the inner side, there is an exit for the fire air and smoke to escape up the chimney. So that the only heat to come directly from the fire into the room is radiant heat from the glowing wood. All the rest is got rid off, up the chimney, to the outside.

Meanwhile, back at the air chamber, things are hotting up – as they would with all those hot flames curling round it. These warm the hot air inside the chamber, which rises by convection and is led by the nose out into the room, heating it. Fresh air from the cellar comes up to replace it.

By these means, Franklin was able to have it both ways – he got the maximum heat out of his fire, and transferred this to the room without causing draughts or stuffiness.

Having laid the trail towards better wood burning, Franklin made way for other chaps to come along and carry things stages

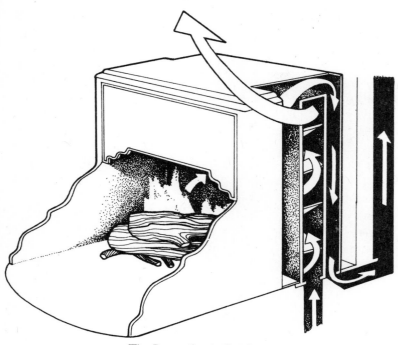

The Pennsylvania fireplace

further. Which a multitude of them did, far too many to work through here. Indeed, in a sense, there is no need. For all these eager beaver woodophiles led themselves very neatly into a trap.

I can illustrate this well enough with the tale of Dr Arnott and his Thermometer stove. Dr A. was an English doctor of 1838 vintage – at least, he was at the time of this tale. He was one of a horde of amateur inventors who could not resist having a go, just for the love of it. No reward or profit was expected to come from these labours. Just the warmth of having improved mankind's lot in the vale of tears, woes and chilly posteriors department.

In the Arnott stove the main casing is divided into an upper and lower chamber. The only connection between these is a pipe that has a sealed end in the upper space. In this pipe is a self-regulating mercury valve. Between the two chambers is the fire bed, which has no contact with the outside casing. Air is fed from the bottom end of the pipe directly into the base of the fire. When the fire is lit, the hot gases and flames from it are led unprotestingly up, down and around the inside of the upper chamber by means of baffles, rather like those mazes built by the Elizabethans from which uninformed persons can never find the way out. Of course, there is a way out, and the hot emissions eventually find it, escaping with relief up the chimney. The idea behind all that is that the longer you can keep the hot stuff inside the fire case, the more heat you can extract from it to radiate as warmth into the outside room.

As the fire gets hotter, the air in the sealed part of the pipe expands. From the diagram of Dr Arnott's stove on page 18 you will see that the bottom end of the sealed pipe ends in a cup filled with mercury. This is the self-regulating mercury valve. The onward connection running round and down to the fire bed dips into this cup. Under normal running conditions it does not dip down as far as the level of the mercury. So, as the fire burns it is able to suck in the necessary air supplies through this pipe. As the fire grows hotter and the air in the sealed pipe expands, this pushes down on the mercury, which, as you would expect, is forced to rise up in the cup. It rises high enough to cover the opening into the fire-air pipe. No air gets down to the fire, which dies down and cools. The air in the sealed pipe cools, contracts and eases the pressure on the mercury. The mercury in the cup falls back. The fire air pipe is opened up again, air whizzes down, the fire perks up, begins to get hotter, the air in the sealed pipe expands and so on.

But seemingly, a nifty wheeze, and, as the report in *The Saturday Magazine* (31 March 1838) concludes:

Among the advantages of the Thermometer stove, we may mention that it maintains an uniform temperature if required at night as well as by day, but which can be increased or diminished in a few minutes. The fire within it may be kept alight without requiring attendance or any additional fuel for ten, or even a greater number of, successive hours. To warm a moderate-sized room, the cost of fuel will not exceed a penny a day. No smoke, dust, vapour, or other products of combustion, can possibly escape into the room.

The air is warmed, not heated, and hence it is not deprived of its health-preserving properties. There is no danger attending the use of the Thermometer stove; it is more easily managed than an open fire; and there is no waste either of fuel or heat.

Honestly, you might almost think the chap was writing a puff for a modern stove. And it does read well. Except, that it doesn't work. Here we come back to the trap that I was talking about.

At first sight it seems the most logical thing that holding back the hot gases from the fire inside the stove casing will extract more heat from it and make the fire work better. But this ignores one vital function. It is the rising up of the hot gas in the chimney that creates the draught at the base of the fire. As the hot gas billows out at one end, it pulls in fresh cold air at the other. Without supplies of fresh air full of nourishing oxygen, the fire won't burn.

Therefore – and I apologise for imposing a firm therefore on you at this stage, but it is necessary – therefore, if you squeeze and soak all the heat out of the fire gas inside the casing, by the time it reaches the bottom end of the chimney flue it will have very little zoomability left. Cool to warm gas doesn't rise as rapidly as the hot stuff.

Alert and attentive readers will point out that that can't be important, since draught dampers are already installed at the bottom of the fire to cut down the intake of air.

All very true. But you cannot damp down a draught if there is no draught to be damped. The effect of partly closing a bottom damper is, not only to reduce the volume of what is coming in, but to increase the speed of the air flow inwards, and to concentrate it into particular parts of the fire. If there is no appreciable draught to start with, this can't, won't and doesn't happen.

This tale of Dr Arnott's Thermometer stove strikes right to the core of modern closed-stove design. It is what present-day designers ponder over, balancing how much you take out of the fire against how much it is necessary to leave in.

Indeed, when you come right down to it, there has hardly been a new idea in stove design for a century and a half. The

The Franklin stove

first airtight stove seems to date from 1836. The bimetallic thermostat, now featured on modern Scandinavian and American stoves, was first thought of by Elisha Foote of Geneva, New York in 1842. And even though earlier I placed much of the responsibility for the improved enclosed fire on the shoulders of Benjamin Franklin, it is clear that he was building on the ideas and experiments of a host of other people, although it is his name that is attached to that kind of fire in the USA – one enclosed in a metal casing with double, front-opening doors. The fire can be used with the doors either open or closed, although in the latter position, the fire's efficiency is just about doubled, as I hope you have by now grasped.

The reason why I have dragged you by your fire dogs through this mass of turgid explanation is that sooner or later, if you are to pursue your membership of the wood-stove club, you must choose your own stove.

How to begin? At least you can now read the sales literature with a more quizzical eye, thrusting your mental probes deep into the soft flesh of flashy claims made by the sales lads. Ask yourself all the time: Will it work? Can it work? Does it work?

When you get to whatever wood stove display you eventually find your way to, squat down and peer into the belly of the fire under consideration. Visualise the pattern, the flow. The fire burns here – air comes in here – the flames rise up there – curl over this baffle – are diverted by that. Eventually, they reach the flue exit. In what condition? By how much have they been held back?

Now we must cut back to the chimney situation to examine in detail another matter previously touched upon. Tar. The first wood fire I lit was an old Jotul 118 – a simple box fire with a rather long casing. My ignorance of wood fires was total. I remember crouching in front of the beast wondering how it was to be ignited. Remembering my childhood, I screwed up paper and covered this with twigs. Then a layer of small wood pieces. I put a match to it, closed the stove door, waited, and was astounded when in a few moments a comfortable roar was heard to come from the stove. It did not occur to me that there was a damper in the stove door that could be closed to advantage. For me, in my ignorance, it was enough that the fire worked, could be reliably lit each time with this simple paper-and-twigs technique. So, even though it was early autumn with lovely limpid warm evenings, I ran the fire wide open, opening all the doors and windows to keep it company.

When you burn wood, as when you burn anything else, there remains the left-over ash. Everyone knows that. From time to time ash has to be removed. Everyone knows that. Except me. It was at least a month of nightly burnings before it dawned on me I had not removed any ash. I peered into the casing. There was ash to be seen, a thickish layer of about an inch in depth. But it never got any thicker. Week after week, still just that one inch of ash. How come?

It took me a while to work it out. The 118 is a plain old box stove, and to stop the hot stuff from the fire whirling straight up the chimney, there is a baffle plate angled above the fire. But on my model this was missing. With the front damper wide open, and no baffle in the fire chamber, the heat roared up the flue with powerful fury. Enough fury to take with it surplus fragments of ash. No doubt some accident of the air flow pattern kept an inch of fine grey powdery residue lying along the bottom of the casing. Otherwise, the draught was forceful enough to whip out everything else, leaving the chamber bare.

If a fire in that condition can dispose of ash, you may imagine its effect on minute deposits of tarry fluid vapourised in the fire's heat. With the flames spurting up the chimney with undiverted vigour making the chimney wall oven-top hot, not a fragment or flake of it would have condensed and lodged there. Visual inspection confirms this diagnosis. In the flue to which the 118 was attached there is no sign of tar. Equally, the inside of the fire chamber is as dry as an Egyptian tomb.

Some wood-burning persons actually advocate leaving the flue damper – if one is fitted – permanently wide open, controlling the size and energy of the fire by means of the bottom air-damper controls.

But, enough of theory. Let me try to apply, for your delectation and delight, some of these theoretical ideas in a practical way. The most practical issue that comes to my mind at this point is the stove you are going to buy. A choice must be made. Let's get at it.

At the last count – and this changes almost daily – there were 17 basic box stoves on sale in the UK. They range from the Lange Hamlet from Denmark – in the £250-bracket – (prices change almost every week) plus a delivery charge if you get it from the main agents and not from a local dealer – to the bottom end of the price range and the Enterprise BH25 from Canada at something under £100.

Between these two extremes there is a wide range of choice. What is best? One item that influences cost is the method of manufacture. There are two main techniques. Expensive stoves tend to be made of cast-iron plates bonded together. Cheaper models come in welded steel plate. Purists argue that cast iron

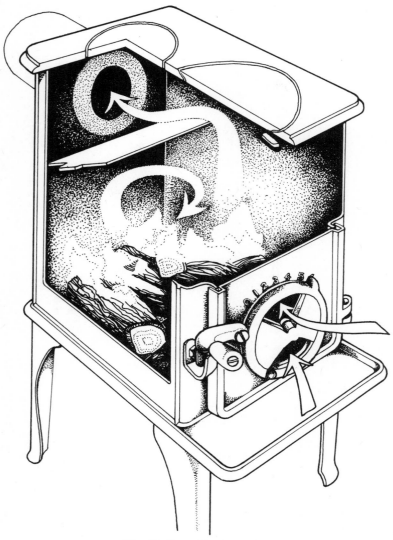

The Trolla 103 box stove

lasts longer than welded steel. It is a question of what longer means. All the classic stove models I have seen of the past two centuries have been made of cast iron. So it lasts that long. But that evidence tells one very little. One knows nothing of how the stove was worked, how often – daily or at infrequent intervals – how hot, with what wood fuel, how thick a layer of ash, and so forth. These days of built-in obsolesence do not condition one to expect any consumer durable to last for longer than 20 years of continuous use. There does not seem to be any evidence to contradict the expectation that a properly run welded-steel stove will not last that long.

So, why pay more than the cheapest? Two reasons. Quality of manufacture and effectiveness of design. Take the first one first.

The important – vital even – aspect of a box stove (or any other closed wood-burning stove, for that matter) is its airtightness. If air can leak into the chamber not only will this negate the control of its burning qualities, but will prevent the fire staying in for extended periods of time. The fire will always be burning faster and hotter than you may want. Of course, in terms of tar control you might argue that this is a good thing. But it is hard to make out a case for fire management being by happenstance rather than your finger being on the damper.

So, your first task when coming face to face with the possible stove of your choice in the showroom is to lower yourself to the floor, open its door, shove your eyes as close inside as you can manage and see if you can see any gleams of light. Almost certainly you won't see any, but be sure.

From my experience, however, there are very few really bad models on the market. Some are better than others and there is a certain safety in sticking to a well-known, established name. But many small works are turning out excellent models with names that few have heard of before. It is a pity that the wood stove manufacturers and major importers have not yet set up a trade organisation that could lay down standards of quality control and manufacture. But there are rumbles in the undergrowth and perhaps by the time this book reaches your hands something will have been done about that.*

*They now have: W.A.R.M. – Woodburning Association of Retailers and Manufacturers, P.O. Box 35, Stoke-on-Trent ST4 7NU.

Ulefos 172

(*above*) Pither Forester (*below*) Logfire Warwick

The most likely source of air leaks into your box stove will be the front door. Cheaper models rely just on a close fit. The more expensive jobs have doors that are ground to fit exactly, and this air seal is reinforced with an asbestos gasket fitted round the edge. The door handle will engage in some kind of lock to hold the door absolutely tight. So, your second task is to check the solidity of the door, how well it fits and locks, and if the lock jams or can easily and smoothly be opened. I say this because when a fire is hot the metal in the casing expands. This includes the door lock. One that opens at a touch when cold may be the very devil to shift when hot. Try, therefore, to see the model you are considering laying out hard cash for alight before you sign the purchase order.

While you have been casting your glimmers over the outside and innards of the stove on the witness stand, you will have noted a baffle plate inside angled above the fire, and in the front loading door there will be some type of air-control damper. In the better models the air damper has an upper and lower entry. The Trolla 103 burning behind me as I write has a circular disc that rotates, disclosing upper and lower openings. These can be wide open or totally closed. It being a circular control, the upper and lower entries are always open the same amount.

A box stove burns – not from top to bottom – but from front to rear. And I am explaining this here so that you can do what I recommended earlier: visualise the air flow through the fire to judge its effectiveness.

When you set the match to your paper screws and kindling you will see that the flame streams backwards into the fire box. When you close the fire door, the only way air can get to the fire is through the damper control, wide open at this point. The fire sucks air in and so spreads itself backwards along the bed of the fire box. At the back the only place it can go is up. Its natural inclination is to spurt up into the chimney flue. But this is where the baffle plate is fitted to hinder this happening. The hot air is forced to move forwards again back towards the entry door. So, now you have two fire layers – a bottom one in which cool air is moving backwards through the fire, and an upper layer where hot air is moving towards the front. Why?

The first burning is quite inefficient. The wood is not yet hot. Only its surface is gasified. Few of the volatiles are ignited. By moving air through the fire – backwards along the fire bed and forwards again to the upper part of the air damper entry – those parts of the fuel gases that have not been completely burnt are brought back to make contact with a secondary air supply, namely the second layer of air that is being sucked in. This hot unburnt gas gets a boost of hot oxygen, enough to set it alight. The long curling flames from this second burning are evidence that the fire emission is even hotter than before. It wants to rise. Where can it go? Only so far as the top of the casing, at which level it makes its way back again to the rear where it escapes up the chimney flue. All clear thus far?

If all that seems a bit complicated, look at it this way. Assume you are peering into the fire case from the side. Taking a line from the air damper entry at the bottom right-hand corner, via the angled baffle plate at the top left corner, with the chimney flue exit just above it, the fire gas executes an S-shaped path, backwards, forwards, backwards again. Of course, this S-pattern varies with the design of the baffle and the heat of the stove. The Jotul type of baffle, running almost the full length of the inside casing, produces a pronounced S-path. The much shorter, inclined baffle of the Trolla results in a thicker, fatter S.

When the fire is hot, the S-bend diversion is much greater than when the stove is burning more slowly. In the latter case, in the Trolla, there is hardly very much of an S at all, and you might conclude that the main effect of the baffle is to prevent flames rising into the chimney and so wasting their heat. With a slow-burning fire, the baffle tends to create a dead spot at the bottom rear of the fire chamber, which can be confirmed by the accumulation there of small pieces of partly burned wood, like charcoal.

Nonetheless, the general accuracy of this description of what is going on inside the box stove can be confirmed by a simple test. After the fire is lit, check the temperature of the stove panels with the palm of your hand. You will find that the top, front of the box is getting hot before the bottom side panels are even becoming faintly warm.

The firebed firing is called the first or primary burning. This is where the heat comes from in traditional, primitive fires. All the technological advances of the past two centuries have been directed towards organising the additional, secondary burn. A good deal of a stove designer's skill goes into getting the balance between these two right. If there is not a proper secondary burn, about half – sometimes more than half – of your potential heat is wasted up the chimney in the open air. When you try to visualise how this burning pattern might take place inside a box stove, compare one design with another. Ask yourself why one baffle is shaped differently from another. Why is it placed in a different position, at a different angle? Which looks to your eye as if it will shove hot gas around inside the most effectively? Better still, inspect the stoves when they are both alight. See which throws off the most heat. Some vendors are reluctant to start fires in their stoves. As one put it to me: 'I'm not in the business of creating secondhand models.' Fair point. All the same, other ventures seem able to produce working models to convince the cash-carrying public that their's is better than Joseph Bloggaramus's down the road.

Now that the box-stove pattern is in your mind we can move on to the next category up – the box stove with heat exchanger. There are eight such types on sale in the UK. These range from the low-price Mørso Horatio from Belgium to the massive Ulefos 172 from Norway priced at about £600.

Essentially, these are basic box stoves with a bit extra added on the top. This extra is a second chamber, usually in the form of a hollow archway. The idea is that when the hot stuff from the fire has swirled about inside the lower box casing, as I hope I have described to your satisfaction, it wafts up into the second chamber on top. As it moves through this upper storey, it makes the metal walls or casing hot, and this additional heat is passed on to the house or room being heated by radiation.

All this is something like pressing grapes for wine. The lush bunches come in from the vineyards and are given the first pressing when a great quantity of juice gushes out. But not everything. Because when all the hearty grape-growing chaps have had a breather, they get down to giving the mushed fruit, pips and stalks a second going over. From this second pressing comes almost as much juice again as from the first.

But with wood-burning stoves there is a snag – one that stove designers take a good deal of time and trouble to balance out. From what I have already described you can more or less work it out for yourself. The speed with which the fire gas charges up the chimney relates to its heat. The hotter it is, the faster it dashes to get out. The more rapidly it leaves the fire, the more speedily does fresh air come in at the bottom, making the fire burn hotter, more efficiently and with diminished tar, if any at all. If by this second squeezing of heat the hot gas is cooled so much that it only rises slowly in the chimney, then you can see that all the other working arrangements further down will diminish. This possibly explains why this type of stove has not been a front-runner in UK sales. All the same, don't discount them too readily. The Scandinavians in particular have used them for years with success. Try to see one alight and judge for yourself if, in the conditions prevailing in your house, such a model might work well.

This brings me to the third, and probably the most popular, category of stove available. Again, it is a variation on the box-stove theme.

There is something particular to British stove persons that doesn't seem to pop up among stove persons abroad. I've mentioned it before because I notice it in myself. We like to be warm, to feel warm. But true comfort does not come to us unless we can actually see the source of the warmth. For others it is enough to see the box stove merrily burning away in the corner and to visualise all the hot activity bursting away inside. Not so for your average UK citizen. To satisfy his craving, manufacturers for the past century have put on the market stoves with windows. A hundred years ago they used small sheets of mica, or, to give it its full name, mineral silicate. This separates into thin leaves, the transparent forms of which are known as isinglass. Mica stands up to heat, or rather, it stands up to heat better than any other substance available a hundred years ago. But, there are disadvantages. Heat causes it to discolour and become more opaque. And, after a time it becomes brittle. None of this applies today, of course, because we have the tough ovenware type of glass that stands up to extremes of heat and that does not discolour or turn brittle. As a result, one of the most recent types of wood stove to come on the market is the glass-fronted model. Again, there is a wide range of choice. The cheapest is the British made Pither Forester, the largest is the English Logfire Warwick.

As these stoves have glass windows it is easy enough to see what goes on inside. You can follow the curl and curve of the long, yellow, feathery volatile flames, with the small, whiter, sharper wood flame burning at their base. The resins, oils and other chemicals in the wood will often produce clear blue or green flames for a short while.

It is time I said something about heat ratings. On all the sales literature there will be a heat output rating for each model. This will sometimes be expressed in British Thermal Units (BThUs) or Kilowatts. No wood stove manufacturers or importing agents seem yet to have adopted the EEC unit of energy – the joule.

To a large extent, these heat output ratings are a nonsense. For a start, there is no standard way of arriving at a figure, of measuring a stove's heat potential. Indeed, some sales agents treat these figures so casually, that I have known circumstances where a figure on a brochure has been altered at the stroke of a pen, either up or down, just to satisfy some presumed sales requirement.

What, if anything, do the figures mean? When it is stated that a stove is rated at, let us say, 36,000BThU, the manufacturer or agent wishes to convey that that is the *maximum* sustained output of the stove when it is going at full blast. If you are burning it with the dampers half closed, it will not be producing the same amount of heat. Nor is there any direct correlation between damper setting and heat output. Such a fire burning on a half setting does not necessarily produce 18,000BThU.

Again, this figure assumes ideal conditions for the fire installation. It presumes that your chimney draws well and that on the day when the measurement is taken the wind is blowing from the right direction and that the ambient air temperature and humidity are at standard levels. Again, it must make some kind of assumption about the fuel you are burning, the type and density of wood, its moisture content and so forth.

You will tell me that this must be equally so for coal stoves that are similarly rated. But coal is much more a standard fuel than wood, and one can make quite precise determinations about it, about its size, calorific value and condition.

The figures, I submit, are not in themselves very much of a help – except in a very general sense – in helping you to decide which model of wood stove will meet your needs. What is needed is a rule of thumb that you can carry in your head. I think I can give you one.

Work out roughly the volume of the room or rooms to be heated. Let us say it comes to 2 000 cubic feet – I have worked on a room 20 feet long by 10 feet wide with 10 feet high ceilings, so it is something fairly large for a modern house. The stove that will comfortably heat that volume will have a fire chamber with the same number of cubic inches – i.e., with a fire measuring 20 inches long, 10 inches high and 10 inches deep. If the room you wish to heat is 3 000 cubic feet in volume, the fire you choose should have a chamber roughly 3 000 cubic inches in capacity.

I accept that this is a very rough guide and that it ignores many factors, not least of which is the difference in efficiency between one stove design and another. Quite so. But when you are faced with a bewildering fistful of brochures and a showroom bulging with models, and all the while the sales chap's voice is clacking away in your ear, blinding you with science, my rule of thumb is at least a small piece of science that you can blind him back with!

My rule of thumb also ignores the central heating issue, but I will come back to that (see page 82). For the moment let me get back to the subject of glass-fronted stoves. These are designed to burn from bottom to top, rather than from front to rear as in the box stoves. While you squat watching them burn – wood stove persons tend to do a lot of squatting! – you will notice that the thinking behind the air-flow pattern is different from that I have outlined for the airtight box stoves.

Mostly, the glass fronts take in their air low down at the base of the fire. Generally, although not universally, there is no secondary air intake to feed in at a higher level. The secondary burning is all accomplished on the one delivery of air.

From observation, this is my analysis of what happens. Glass fronts invariably are fitted with a flue damper, some kind of simple butterfly valve in the upper exit into the chimney. When the fire is first lighted, both the upper and lower air dampers are wide open. Water vapour swirls up from the young fire, soon to be followed by the curling yellow flames as the volatiles ignite. These curve away into the flue carrying their heat to the chimney breast and the outside air. At least – not entirely.

The roof of the fire chamber in most glass-fronted stoves is not flat, but formed as a heat trap of some kind. In the case of my Belgian Kamina, the top end of the fire space looks like the underside of a large flattened V. The outer casing here consists of a substantial cast-iron hood. The rising heat from the fire

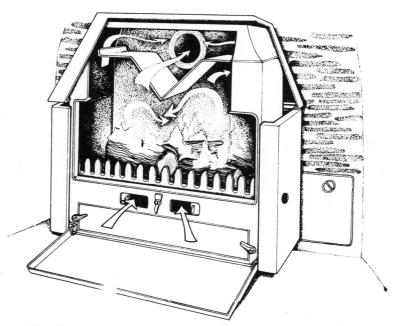

The Kamina glass-fronted stove; note the flue door on the right

warms this – actually it becomes too hot to touch – and the weight of metal is enough to hold the heat, which is then radiated into the living-room. As you sit by the fire you can see the waves of heat rising from this hood.

But, I must get back down to the fire, which is heating up nicely to a long, steady burn. The critical factor is the temperature inside the fire chamber. When this is hot enough for wood to ignite on contact, the time has come to begin to extract the best performance from the appliance, which is maximum heat with not too rapid fuel consumption and minimum tar deposit, if any (see page 94).

The first point to watch for is whether enough air comes in through the bottom air ports to supply oxygen for both the first and second burnings. Make two simple tests. Close the air entry completely. Note the effect on the fire. How much flame remains after five minutes? Does the fire seem to be burning steadily? Is it going out? Open the air entry fully. How quickly does the fire pick up? How soon do the flame patterns return – first the long, volatile flames, then the shorter, firmer wood flames? How long does it take before you can hear air rushing through the air entry?

Here, I must admit to a personal preference. There are two air intake designs commonly found. One consists of a circle of small holes covered by a metal disc. The disc is mounted on a central screw thread. As it is turned, it unscrews away from the air holes in the casing, exposing them and letting in more air. I don't like this. It seems to me that this method lacks fine control. Once the disc is unscrewed a few turns air is going to rush through all the holes. Unscrewing the disc further does not seem to increase the flow proportionately. It is an all or nothing system. I prefer air entries where a small metal plate slides back and forth, making a bigger or smaller hole. This seems, in practice, to give a more precise control.

Next question: is the upper damper effective enough to hold back the flow of hot gas from the fire and retain it inside the stove casing? This is important. Warmth can radiate directly through the glass front. More importantly, it must heat up the casing so as to pass out into the room. Is there enough weight of metal in the casing to retain the heat? Thin casings will heat up quickly and cool down with the same speed. Thick, heavy casings will warm up more slowly, but hold the heat for a long time and cool slowly.

We move on now to the next category of wood-burning stove for your consideration. It may be that you are so attached to the seeing-the-fire philosophy that even the intervention of a glass front seems to cut you off from the source of warmth. You must have direct contact with the fire, in which case, the design for you may be the open stove with metal doors, like the Franklin stove. Closed, this burns at about 75 per cent efficiency. In this condition, it can remain alight all day, keeping the house rooms warm. When evening falls and you want, sentimentally, something cosy to sit by, you have only to open two metal doors at the front of the stove for its gorgeous blaze to be fully revealed to you. Of course, at the same time, its burning efficiency goes down to about 35 per cent, but presumably, if you are wildly keen on open fires, you won't care about that.

Again, in the UK, there are plenty to choose from. Among the best of the larger models is the Woodwarm Firebird stove from Devon; cheapest is the basic Lange Kosi from Denmark.

Critical in your examination of these models is the fit of the doors. As explained before, those coming from the better manufacturers have a tissue-tight fit. Some are even ground to fit and have asbestos packing gaskets. The traditional Colonial style of Franklin stove has four door-panels that swing across on hinges as two pairs, one right, one left. It is important that the main hinges on these models are robust and firm and that those between the panels work easily and will continue to do so when hot.

Somewhere at the top of the market range are the Vigilant and Defiant parlour stoves from Vermont. (These are imported to this country by Morley Marketing, Morley Hall, Ware, Hertfordshire.) The Vigilant is, in effect, a scaled-down version of the larger Defiant. For this last model an interesting claim is made, namely, that by means of interior baffles, it has the longest flame path of any stove currently being sold. Heat from the fire is led up across, around, down and back again before it is allowed to escape through the flue, the total length of this marathon of combustion running to some five feet. I have not run one of these stoves, nor have I seen test results, other than those supplied by the makers, but I have a nagging suspicion that it may have a propensity to produce and secretly harbour tar. It is clear from the design that heroic attempts have been made to deal with this menace. The layout of primary and secondary air entry ports combined with a secondary air tube to feed preheated air to the secondary combustion chamber is evidence of highly sophisticated design strategems.

Do they work? I am willing, and would like, to be convinced. The longer the flame path length the longer it is going to take to rouse the fire to working temperature. Give it a good, solid draught and it will undoubtedly generate gales of heat. But, what happens when it is damped down overnight? All those

The Defiant stove

interior chambers will cool down. Condensation and tar deposits will occur. Will the heat of the next day be enough to burn it clean? I wonder. And once the interior and flue is tarred, only extensive scraping will get it clear. Which means taking the stove to bits.

For me, simplicity is best, within limits. One can be too mean and greedy with a fire, trying to extract from it more than it is able to supply.

Mention of this complexity of internal trunking brings me to another maze of the fire box. If yours is a home with a combined kitchen-diner or an old-fashioned vast kitchen where everyone congregates, then there is another wood stove option you should consider.

Cooker heaters are now arriving from the Continent. Those I have seen come from France, Austria, Germany and Switzerland. Doubtless, there are others. One's first impression is that these are solidly made items. In an age of unenduring consumer durables, these are made to last.

Several I have seen working in country farmhouses have beamed with a warm radiance on the families toasting their toes and tea cakes around them. Marriage guidance counsellors would be well advised to recommend these as a remedy for declining marriages. One of these will keep all the family members busy working it. In return it keeps them warm and provides an array of cookery treats. The stove is never without a large tub of soup quietly bubbling, or a succulent stew simmering somewhere within, while kettles boil on the hotplate almost as quickly as with electricity. My natural admiration for these wood-burning giants is tempered with green envy that I have not, so far, been able to find space for one in my own home.

Talking to those who do have them, working points arise. Like the American Defiant, heat is taken to the ovens in most models by up, over and around trunking. In addition to the considerations I have already raised tarwise, this tends to contract the size of the ovens. On the smallest German Wamsler this is a mere 8 by 13 by 19 inches – adequate for most daily needs but a bit of a squeeze for a turkey.

My formula for stove volume in cubic inches to room volume

in cubic feet is still valid. As an example, the large Franco-Belge cooker-heater has a capacity of just under 3000 cubic inches. It will comfortably heat a kitchen-living room of 3 000 cubic feet. In addition it will feed 15 radiators, supply domestic hot water and, of course, furnish the heat for all cooking, including a hot plate for boiling quick kettles of water.

Obviously, the efficiency of these stoves is high. This is achieved by surrounding the fire with a complete water jacket so that hardly a wisp of heat is wasted. In these stoves it is doubly important that during the working day the temperature of the fire be kept well up. Without this, the efficiency of the fire box will drop markedly, and with such a weight of solid metal surrounding it, the task of bringing the working temperature up, if it should drop, is a pretty long one. In the background there is always the risk of tar at low temperatures.

Ranging from portable barbecue wood stoves, through mini-cookers suitable for holiday homes and caravans, through workshop stoves to multifuel appliances, the variety of wood burning stoves is extensive, but I shall confine myself to mentioning one more in detail. This one is suitable for something resembling a country parsonage or vicarage – the type of place that commonly gets converted to a small country hotel with 10 bedrooms.

There are central heating wood burning boilers of many kinds, but one consists simply of a vast cavern of a fire chamber surrounded by a water jacket. There is one installed here. It requires a room of its own to house it. If one is not available then you must attach a substantial outhouse to your establishment. You will see what I mean when I tell you that the model – a Danish Passat Ho 45 – is 5 feet high, $3\frac{1}{2}$ feet in width, and almost 6 feet long. The fire chamber is large enough for an adult to sit in. It will take logs of almost any diameter up to 5 feet in length, or the equivalent in other fuels, for it can work on any combustible alternative, twigs, bales of straw, cardboard, household refuse, animal droppings. Its wood consumption is about 100 pounds (45 kilos) a day, or about a tonne and a half each month. But for this prodigious intake it will heat 22 radiators, and provide domestic hot water for the kitchen and three bathrooms. Water temperature is kept at between 150°F and 170°F. It is fuelled every morning with a top up last thing at night. Ash needs to be cleared out every two or three months.

I would hardly have had a word to say against this paragon of all the wood-burning virtues had we not now, at the end of a long, hard, non-stop wood-burning winter, encountered our first hiccup. In the firedoor of the Passat is a lower and an upper air flap for the primary and secondary burns. These are controlled by a simple bi-metallic thermostat mounted on the top housing and connected to the flaps by metal chains. As the stove gets hot, the strip expands, eases the pull on the chains and the flaps close. When the stove cools, the strip contracts, pulls on the chains, the flaps open and the fire picks up. Just recently, these flaps have begun to let out smoke. This is why.

During the winter, the inside of the fire chamber has become encrusted with a layer of crisp, brittle black tar. It flakes off at the touch. The cavity is so vast that this does not impede the fire's burning in any way. Perhaps there is a marginal decrease in the transfer of heat through the fire wall to the water jacket, but there is so much surplus heat capacity that this is not noticeable. The tar forms because with a fire of this size it is not practicable to ever have it blazing hotly. The roof of the house would lift off. So, day after day, it slow burns quietly, minding its own business, doing, as you might think, no one harm. Secretly, almost by stealth, it is gathering tar in all its secret places. One of these is in the exit flue to the chimney. There is a butterfly valve here, again, automatically controlled. The slow moving hot gas from the fire passes sluggishly through it, leaving a wake of tarry matter. This has now gunged up the valve so that it is jammed almost shut. Smoke cannot easily get out, and as smoke has to go somewhere it forces its way out through the entry flaps. To a degree this tar can be kept down by using a de-tarring compound. Every now and then, the fire is brought up to a higher heat than normal and a couple of tablespoons of the powder contained in a screw of newspaper is tossed in. There is a chemical reaction with the tar which then vanishes up the chimney.

Unfortunately, we did not start to use this compound until

the end of the winter when tarring was already well advanced. Because of the reduced draught it became increasingly more difficult to raise the fire to the level when detarring takes place. This has permitted a build up of tar around the valve in the flue exit. This, of course, is not inevitable. By proper management of the fire it could have been avoided. But it does point up a difficulty with water-jacketed fires. The water surrounding the fire chamber soaks up the heat and speeds it down the pipes to the radiators and tanks. As a result, the inner wall of the fire hardly ever rises above 220°F. This is in sharp contrast to smaller unjacketed fires, such as the Kamina, where the fire wall temperature can be as high as 600°F, if not higher. This water-cooled inner surface is an ideal place for tar to form. It requires regular detarring and an opening wide of the air intakes for a full half hour in every 24, to prevent it.

If you are determined to go through with this thing, then my suggestion now is that you make your way to the nearest purveyor of wood stoves, making sure the establishment has a decent showroom with a variety of models on display. Perhaps one or two of them may actually be burning! You never know your luck!

Squat down — forget your dignity — and thrust your hands into the interiors of various stoves that catch your eye. Open and close doors, air entry ports, flue dampers, anything that moves. If a salesman appears to move in your direction, batter him with every daft question you can think of. Collect swatches of leaflets. But, most importantly, *make no decision.*

Just as this book is going to the printers, news has come to me of a wood stove that uses a newly patented water heating system that looks to me important enough to be included here as an almost stop press item. The stove exists at this moment only as a prototype. Further development is taking place, but it is expected that it will be available on the market by the time this book is published.

The stove is made by the Woodwarm Company and is designed by Simon Keeping. It uses what is called the pierced

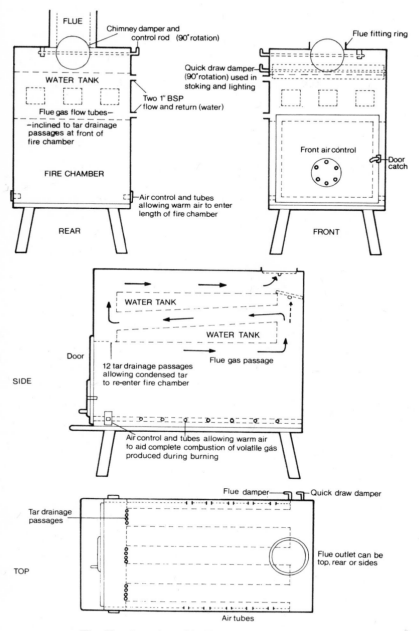

The Keeping pierced-boiler central heating stove

85

boiler. As you can see from the photograph and line drawing (page 85), the unit consists of little more than a large metal box. Mounted inside this box, above the burning area, and tilted downwards from front to rear is the pierced boiler. Rather like a car radiator, it is a flat metal water container through which run a number of square section tubes. Hot air from the fire rises to the boiler, passes along these tubes and is then curled back by baffles to return to the back of the fire where it escapes through the flue outlet. Water in the boiler is heated by the fire gases as they pass along the tubes.

I was invited to attend a demonstration of the prototype. The stove was connected to a house-heating system consisting of ten large radiators. From a cold start, a rough tumble of wood was ignited, the whole central-heating circuit was brought up to sizzling heat – the radiators were too hot to touch with the naked hand – in exactly *six minutes*.

But, there is in addition, another feature. As I have said many times in these pages, the black beast of wood-stove burning is the formation of tar. In this new stove, as I described, the pierced boiler is tilted downwards from front to rear. Along its bottom surface run shallow channels. Hot liquid tar from the wood fire condenses in these channels and runs forward to the front edge. Here there are drip points, and the tar drips back into the fire, and is burned. By this means, the fire chamber is converted into a tar trap. The flue and chimney after several weeks of burning with this prototype model, remain clear of the black tar.

As I said, this stove is the subject of a patent application. It would seem to have a fertile future.

Woodwarm No. 2 (Firefly)

Lange Kosi

(*above*) New Woodwarm Firecracker (*below*) Franco-Belge

4

WHAT STOVE?

Here we are at last – the metal monster glowers across the room at you, and you are wondering if the thing is ever going to work. You have agonised, debated, made up your mind, unmade it, advanced towards a decision, backed away, returned to the showroom for another look, gathered in more brochures, definitely decided for, definitely decided against, wondered if you could afford it, looked at the alternatives . . . and now here you are, finally, with the monster installed and ready to go. Will it light?

My previous experience spanned 15 years of coal-stove lighting, and if you enjoy temperament and uncertainty, then you will enjoy coal stoves. That task begins with a thorough riddle of ash and clinker into the ash pan, which then has to be carefully carried through the house and outside to the ash bin. Next, an acre or so of newspaper must be laid round the stove. It never seems that this precaution can be necessary before you start. But smutty pieces of half-burnt nodules from the previous fire have a way of wandering where they have no business to wander, leaving behind a black trail as evidence of their passing.

There seems to be no better way of removing the dead remains from the grate than by hand. Even if the fire bars are removed, I know of no tool that will winkle out every last remnant of gunge. Heedless of the consequences to your delicate white skin, you plunge your hands in and bring out the remains in ashy fistfuls, dumping them in a handy bucket, taking care that plumes of ash dust do not spurt up in the room and cover the furnishings and fittings.

With the stove now clean and clear you spread a layer of

small anthracite coal on the fire bed. Into this you thrust a minimum of four paraffin wax fire lighters. If it is a bad day for firelighting – and you can never tell – you may need six. With great care you arrange further small pieces of coal over and around the lighters, creating a mound through which air can whistle.

You negotiate a lighted taper through the fire bars, setting fire to one corner of each fire lighter, and continue to build coal piece by piece on top, taking care that the delicate, fluttering flame is not smothered. When you have a decent enough mass of coal, you shut the front door of the stove, open wide the dampers, and go away for at least half an hour.

At the end of that time, if the fire gods have been leaning your way, you will come back to find a dark mass of coal with a small glowing red patch at the base. With luck and careful nurturing, this can be encouraged over the period of another hour or so, to burn up into a fire.

So, you can judge with what trepidation I approached my first wood lighting. I had never done it before and could only guess at the technique. Could I make do without fire lighters? I hoped so. I hadn't got any. The wood consisted of a few rough old pieces that I had picked up in the woods and I also had a supply of dry twigs for kindling together with a copy of yesterday's newspaper.

When you are in a fix, there is nothing more helpful, I find, than a flood of childhood memories. When I was just a thin sliver of humanity there used to come regularly every summer an invitation to visit my auntie in her Sussex cottage. On cool evenings I would sit on the plumpy sofa swinging my legs and watching her light the fire. This was the memory that came flooding back. The technique had been tucked away in my mind just waiting to be used when the time came. A kind of memory-based instinct took over. As if I had been doing the same thing every evening since those distant days, I tore the newsprint into single pages and scrunched them into half tight balls, tight enough not to unfold, but not such hard lumpy little balls that they would not catch light. I spread these across the base of the stove – it was an old Norwegian box stove – heaping them into a single mound. From two of the paper balls I teased an ear to which I could touch a match when the time came. On top of the paper I spread three small handfuls of twigs, covering these with the same area of small wood. As it was my first lighting I took great care how these were arranged. But I needn't have bothered. Later I found wood fires are not the least bit fussy and don't care too much about formal arrangements.

These preparations made, I struck a match, applied it to the paper ears, made sure these had caught, slammed the stove door shut and settled back to await events. I hadn't long to wait. There came almost at once a murmur that crescendoed into a roar. It was as if a physical presence had come into the room, a jolly giant of some kind with something pretty powerful by way of heavy breathing.

There was a circular air vent at the base of the stove door and air was racing through this like a mountain stream through a narrow defile of rocks. Hurtling through. Inside the stove box things were happening, that was very clear. The flat stove top was already almost too hot to touch. The side panels were gaining heat. Cautiously, I opened the stove door. Inside was a mass of flame ranging in colour from an almost white yellow to the deepest red of a misty sunset. Heat bellowed at me like an angry bull, very nearly grilling my eyebrows. If this was wood-fire lighting, I thought, give me more. There was no coaxing needed here. The wood leapt to its task, eager to get at it.

There is a saying among those whose employment is irregular: as one door closes, they comfort themselves, another opens. A silly, self-defeating saying to my mind, and not in any way true. Except here. I had the strongest feeling that I would never again open a coal-stove door, all stove doors I opened would be wood-burning ones.

Much smoke has shot up the flue since that first day, and the stove in which my baptism of wood fire was consecrated now sits in honourable, but temporary, retirement out in the barn. Yet, on that day was laid down the foundations of a theory and practice of wood-fire lighting that has never failed me and that I am about to expound to you now.

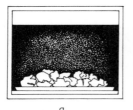 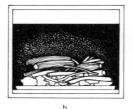 

Lighting a wood fire: (a) screws of paper; (b) twigs and small wood; (c) small logs)

The first magic phrase I wish to toss your way is 'laying and layering'. Mumbo-jumbo, you will think. Or something trite and self-evident. Maybe so, but hear me out, anyway.

We've been all through the fire laying method, which I have not substantially modified since the first time I did it apart from changing the proportions. In my larger fires I use ten screws of paper (which is really only a kind of wood), three handfuls of twigs and enough small wood to cover these with a complete layer. Hang on for a moment – I'll come back to that point.

In my small box fire I put in six screws of paper, two fistfuls of twigs and from six to eight pieces of small wood.

Now, I don't expect you to take my word that this remedy works. I need to take you behind the scenes, as it were, so that what is going on can be seen with abundant clarity. To do that, I have to introduce an item that you might have thought logically should have been included in the last chapter. But, as it could do me a useful service, I have held it back until now.

For the most part this book is about wood stoves, and by historical derivation and convention that has come to mean, virtually, airtight stoves. That, certainly, is how I have used the term. But there are modern, open wood-fire grates that have a role to play. Generically, they derive from the fire place that Ben Franklin devised in America in the eighteenth century. The young Benjamin had been told of the blazing fireplaces of the traditional British country home. In and around his native Philadelphia he saw those of the German emigrant families. When he devised something more efficient and less wasteful, these were the starting points of his design. In Franklin's design, you will recall, air was sucked up from the cellar, warmed round the fire and came out into the room as an additional source of heat.

There is currently on the UK market a modern variation of Benjamin Franklin's stove. The fire comes as a complete unit, a box within a box, the whole forming an open fire. The inner box is, in effect, the housing for the wood fire. Between the inner and outer box is an air space. Air is sucked in by convection through an entry below the fire. It circulates up through the space between the two boxes and is fed back into the room through a slot placed centrally above the fire. So, the economically-minded wood-burning person, having opted for the most economical fuel, now finds a way of getting two bites at his cherry.

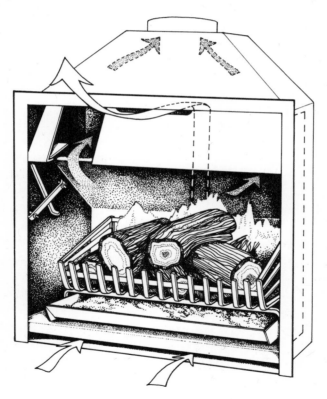

The Jetmaster fireplace

However, even this is not as wholly efficient as an airtight stove, and my reason for shoving it in here for your attention is that, being an open fire, we can see clearly what goes on.

When lighting it in the normal way, the paper flares up and then dies down somewhat, as the ash of the dead paper clogs the flame. But it picks up and spreads steadily down beneath the wood. Quantities of greyish smoke begin to rise up. This is quite complicated stuff to analyse, but a good deal of it is water vapour. This comes in two ways. First water is a byproduct of the chemical process of burning wood. In addition, the gathering heat is starting to drive out the natural moisture in the wood. You will begin to hear a sturdy hissing sound from the wood as the water is driven off. The ends of some of the logs may start to bubble as the water is squeezed out from them.

You might think that water and burning are incompatible. So they are to a degree, but something odd also happens. Water is chemically composed of hydrogen and oxygen. In small doses, heat breaks down water into these two elements, and the oxygen feeds the flame of the fire.

I came across an interesting confirmation of this point. There is an elderly farmer near me who always keeps a couple of logs floating in his pond. When he lights his vast open log fire, one of the sodden logs is placed at the back of the fireplace. Far from putting the fire out, it is claimed the water in the wood helps the fire burn more brightly and throws out more heat. Not having a large fireplace, I have not been able to check this. But certainly, in these early stages of fire lighting, the flame and water vapour spurt up with equal vigour.

By now, the twigs have begun to glow red. Yellowish flames from them curl up round the small wood, leaving long smears of black on their barky flanks. This mass of flame may look robust and healthy. But, don't deceive yourself. The fire is not yet alight. These flames come from the volatiles – the natural oils and resins in the wood – and, incidentally, the source of the wretched tar. These yellow flames will continue to rise and rage up the flue like nerveless fingers plucking their way out. Don't pay them any attention. Set your gaze lower down around their base. This is where the real action is about to begin.

A wood fire burning: (a) water vapour fumes; (b) flaming volatiles; (c) feathery volatile flames and small hard wood flames

Around the edges of the black 'first burns', along the side of the log pieces, there will now appear small, hard, whitish flames. In contrast to the yellow flames that waver and dance, these are brisk, bustling and hardly flicker at all. They signal the fact that the wood fibre is now aflame, and all in your fire garden is lovely.

The smoke emission is now much smaller. Even with an open fire it is often quite hard to see any smoke at all. Of course, a lot depends on the design of your fireplace, the heat of the fire, the type and size of wood you are burning, to name just a few. But an honest, well-caught fire, gives more evidence of its life by flame than smoke.

The next important thing is to get to recognise the crucial moment when refuelling is ideal. You develop a kind of instinct. You don't have to sit there watching the blaze like a hawk. You can hear the right moment.

This is what you are trying to judge. If you put fresh wood on too early, the fire will build up beyond what you need to keep the room at an easy heat. The place will become as overheated as an Amazonian jungle and you will waste fuel. Yet, if you leave the fire and allow it to burn too low, the new logs will take a long time to warm up, catch alight and throw out heat. Meantime, your dwelling and habitable space are getting cold.

There is a simple way of checking if your judgement is right. If, when you put fresh, dry wood on the fire, the long yellow flames from its volatiles curl up almost immediately, but there is no wood flame then you are probably about right.

The pattern unfolds in accordance with this scenario. The fire having caught, the yellow flames slowly die down while the white flames consolidate. The wood glows redder and redder. Shortly after the yellow flames have vanished and there is nothing but wood flame, you begin to get the feeling the fire has lost its urge. Black flameless patches are starting to appear along the sides of the logs – this is the black of charcoal, or half-consumed wood – but the heat of the fire is still there, still strong.

When new wood is put on, this heat is sufficient to ignite the oils and resins. But these are burning just on the surface of the wood. The interior of the new logs is still cool. Heat gradually spreads through the wood. As each layer reaches the required temperature, the hard white wood flame breaks out. And the cycle repeats itself for as long as you keep tossing on wood.

What I have described to you is the theory and practice of wood-fire burning that I call 'layering'. When you lay the fire you put down a proper foundation in layers – paper, twigs, small wood, logs. The fire grows up through these almost like a plant. Its roots are in the hot glowing fire bed. It takes in oxygen from the air surging through it, and, as a plant, it grows.

At any given moment you can appraise the state of your fire by considering what is going on in the layers. Is there a sound foundation? Or, despite hungry roaring, is the fire top heavy, with no base? If so, as a house will collapse, so will your fire. It will tumble down in a shower of sparks and fade rapidly unless you take quick action.

It is good to judge where to toss each piece of new wood. Gauge its size and weight, and throw it into a space where it will lock with other wood and preserve the structure of the fire. If you have got it right, its weight will oblige the ashy, half-burned wood beneath it to collapse. This base layer of hot ash is the foundation of your fire. Above it the wood burning layers and the volatile layers pull the air up to sustain heat.

This pull of air through the fire is important. You can see it work. You can make it work for you. When you place fresh wood on the fading logs, its presence alone is enough to provoke fresh vitality to the blaze. This comes from the venturi effect – when a given volume of moving air is passed through a confined space its speed accelerates; this is what takes place if you lay your logs with due care and understanding. You create smaller spaces between the pieces of wood on the fire and the air coming up through the fire speeds up between them and roars slightly more loudly.

This is what I meant when I said you could hear the correct moment for putting on more wood. The roar of the fire quietly fades; the new wood brings it up again.

Just as it is important to get the layering of the fire right, so equally, one must see that the fire spreads the full width of the fire chamber. Logs are linear items – they have more length than thickness – and naturally, wood fires tend to be linear in shape. (If you are working with thick chopped wood chunks, this won't apply. I'll deal with you later.)

When you face your fire from the front, when you are layering it, lighting it and feeding it when alight, you will, with time, begin to recognise what I like to call 'the ideal profile'. The fire takes on a side-to-side shape. Flame has spread from the centre to the extremities. The full length of the fire is doing its job of producing and throwing out heat.

There are two profiles you should avoid. The most obvious is a fire that piles up in the centre and falls away sharply on each side – like a mountain – a steep central peak with sloping shoulders. A fire with this profile will throw out a mass of heat from the centre, but little from the flanks. These will die rapidly – flames shrinking into blackness while the centre still roars away. Don't tolerate it. Thrust your sturdy poker into the blaze and give it a hefty twitch, pushing the burning embers away from the centre so that they re-ignite the black bits on the edge.

The opposite undesirable is an outline in which the centre is dead and flame spurts up at each side. You have, in effect, something like two small fires. Again, the answer is to shove the fire embers in to the centre and lay fresh logs along them to restore the balanced profile in which the fire is, as near as dammit, the same height along its full length. Maximum heat and best use of your fuel.

How do you deal with chunky bits of wood? Some wood burners are content to have two or three of these leaning together in a slouching kind of way, their tops touching, from

97

which peak a thin spiral of smoke saunters up. That is not my way at all. I am all for the roar and bustle approach with waves of heat slapping briskly around your person. To achieve this I put my chunks together to form, as closely as possible, long shapes. If the chunks are of about equal length, then stagger them when you pile them on the fire, so that the gaps between them don't come immediately one above the other. That way you will oblige the rising hot air to snuggle in and around the chunks and keep them burning briskly.

Of course, all these observations of mine have been keyed to the open stove and you will be wondering how they apply to the airtight jobs I have been recommending. Nothing changes — except that with the closed metal doors, you can't see what is going on inside the stove, and with a glass front you can.

The procedure for lighting an airtight stove is the same as for the open grate — paper screws, twigs or kindling, small wood, logs. Light the two paper ears and retire immediately.

It makes no difference what shape or design of stove you are using. The basic principle remains unaltered. From the instant you apply your match to the makings, you are urging the fire to burn its way up through the various layers. Once alight, you want it to burn with equal strength along the full length and width of the stove regardless of its shape.

One of the reasons for having an airtight stove is so that the wood will burn slowly when required and stay alight for long periods of time, overnight if necessary. There is a useful rule of thumb here, to judge how long your fire will stay in if pushed to the extreme. The very best kind of stove, working at its maximum efficiency will, on a lowest setting, consume about one pound of good wood fuel per hour. So if you put 36 pounds of best quality, dry, hard wood into a well adjusted stove, burning in ideal conditions, it will stay in for 36 hours. That is a maximum. Anything that gets in the way of this best performance will cause the wood to burn more rapidly, and so last for a shorter period.

For slow burning of this kind a good thick bed of wood ash is helpful, in that it holds the heat and helps to keep the fire going at a slow, even rate. However, when you want to open dampers and get a bit of a hot urge into the fire, then the ash bed is a hindrance. It clogs the air passages and clamps down on the burning. Something of a mixed blessing. I have found that for ordinary, hot, daytime burning it is best to work with very little ash. If the ambient temperature in your fire box or chamber is high enough – and I mean, so hot that the outside casing is too hot to touch – then you will find you can work with no ash at all, and not even lighted embers. It is possible to throw a fresh log into a hot empty chamber and it will spontaneously burst into flame (see note at end of chapter).

My routine for daily running with a glass-fronted stove is to open the dampers to a halfway setting in the morning when I get up. The fire will pick up in a few minutes. Fresh wood can be loaded as needed.

When the fire is burning well you can scrabble about inside it with a poker and work some of the dead ash down into the ash pit or tray below the fire. If your model has neither of these, the procedure is slightly more cumbersome. You work the burning fire to one side of the chamber. With a small shovel you lift out ash from the dead side. Then reverse the procedure.

Incidentally, when cold, all wood ash should go straight on your garden. It does wonders for your vegetables.

If you happen to have a glass-fronted stove, slow burning will cause the glass front to occlude and turn opaquely black. For some, the remedy is to open up the dampers and let the fire rip. This clears away the accumulated tar and some of the deposit on the glass. For many this will be enough to keep the glass reasonably clear. Any small tar deposits that form will probably not get larger and will burn away in time. However, since the main point of having a glass front is that you should be able to see the fire, a black encrusted doorway gets in the way rather.

There is another remedy. The glass can be cleaned with a small basin of warm water and a Brillo soap pad. Don't do it when the glass is hot, else you might find yourself the proud owner of an open stove with a glassless door. If you are lighting your stove daily, clean the glass before lighting. Stoves kept in overnight are best cleaned first thing in the morning when the glass is just warm. Of course, you will have to work quickly. With the glass door open, the overnight embers will rapidly pick up to a blaze hot enough to drive you back.

Dip the Brillo pad in a small amount of warm water – a teacup full will do, provided you can be sure not to spill it – and work it across the inside face of the glass lightly, without pressing hard. Most of the black stuff will come away at once. Only a small patch here and there will have hardened with heat. Rub these carefully until all the muck has gone. The entire operation, if you are a slow mover like me, will take about a minute. Swifter fisted persons will flick through in seconds.

This done, take a kitchen sponge, dip a corner in the previously mentioned warm water (teacup of) and remove the dissolved ticky-tacky from the glass. End with a brief lick and a promise.

Contrary to popular belief, this technique does not scratch the oven glass. As a matter of fact, the constant cleaning does seem to inhibit the forming of further black deposits. If the tar is baked hard by heat, it can be softened and dissolved by dabbing it with ordinary household paraffin. Stubborn patches can be removed by scraping gently with the flat blade of a kitchen knife.

Some stoves, particularly modern reproductions of nineteenth-century models, faithful to the original design, have panels of mica in their doors. (I have spoken of this before.) The thing about mica is that it does not seem to collect quite as much tar as glass. On the other hand – and quite a large other hand it is, too – mica discolours with heat. It also turns brittle, flakes and does all kinds of unfortunate things, so my advice is to stick to glass.

All these remarks of mine have been founded on one monumental assumption, that is that you are using dry wood. Wood fires are best lit and run with dry wood. But, as I have experienced during this past, evil-minded winter, circumstances sometimes conspire against this.

I moved into this house in the autumn. The reputation of these broad and bulging acres of south Devon is for winters as mild as doe's breath. I felt no frantic compulsion, therefore, to

100

buttress the household fires against the dead, cold days to come. Each day a supply of wood had to be brought in from somewhere. That somewhere could be anywhere in the surrounding woodland. A supply meant enough wood to fill one compartment in the giant wood box standing just inside the front door.

When fortune beamed as happened when, deep in the woods, one stumbled across a neat stack of logs ready cut and left behind by some previous, forgetful, wood person, one was able to get ahead by as much as two or three days. When we turned winter's corner and the days began to edge longer, we had got ahead to the tune of about a week's supply, cut and ready to burn, with about the same amount dripping outside, waiting to be cut.

Our good fortune is that we are surrounded by neglected woodland. This supplies what was described to us when we bought the place as free fuel. However, as we discovered, when you are at the start of your wood-burning career, free is not necessarily free. Money it may not cost, but time and effort it does.

Trees that are still alive are disqualified for the wood cutter's saw. The green, still living wood is too wet and resiny to burn well. It will throw up the contagion of tar in abundance.

For immediate consumption dead wood is needed. And dead wood is not necessarily dry. Fallen branches can have lain in the mud for a year or two. If the wood has been on the ground that long, much of it may be rotten. Soon you get to know the sickly-sweet smell of decaying wood.

The smell comes from the release of resins. Wood that has decayed is wood that has lost most of the oils and other aromatic substances of which it is made, leaving behind just the dead husk of fibre. This is vulnerable to the seeping attacks of moisture. Rotten wood soaks it up like a beer drinker on a binge and is the very devil to dry out. Green wood – the fresh living stuff – holds about 50 per cent of water. Cut it, stack it, and leave it to air dry for a year or so. At the end of that period the moisture content will have gone down to 20–25 per cent. But it is still between a quarter and a fifth water.

101

Back in the days of the classic cabinet makers in the eighteenth century, this moisture was something for concern, as wood panels containing moisture would warp over the years. They, therefore, laid it down as a code of practice that all wood supplies supplied to them should be properly air-dried.

The definition of properly air-dried wood was wood that had been standing under cover, exposed to the air, for the required period of time, namely, two years for every inch of thickness, plus two years. A smallish trunk measuring two feet across the trunk at the thickest point would have to stand in the open air for 50 years before being considered suitable for cabinet making.

Wood merchants got a bit shirty at this arrangement. A chap might come into the business and be retiring from it at the ripe old age of 60, before some of his best stock was ready to be sold. Too much capital was getting itself tied up. If a sudden rush of trade came from the Chippendale and Hepplewhite enclaves, there was no possibility of fresh batches of wood being rushed through.

Kiln drying was introduced as a way of speeding things up, for wood that had been subjected to a day or so of exposure to the kiln's sturdy heat could be expected to have most of the moisture in it squeezed out. Even then, there remains about an 8 per cent moisture content in wood. You simply cannot get rid of it.

Yet, if wet wood is all you have to work with, you must do the best you can. When lighting a fire it can be reasonably assumed that the newspaper is dry – no problem there. On this you are going to lay damp kindling. Imagine the effect. If you then compound the problem by layering wet small wood on the damp kindling, all that will happen when you apply the necessary match to the paper ears is that the paper will light, white plumes of water vapour will momentarily saunter upwards to the flue. And then the fire will die. Wet fire makings need a boost. The best I have come across is the white, waxy paraffin fire lighters you can buy in packs at grocers, hardware stores and supermarkets. Place one of these between the paper layer and the kindling twigs. Light the paper ears as ordinarily.

The heat generated between the paper and twigs will, in due course, ignite the fire lighter. This will keep flaming long enough to dry out a small portion of wood and induce a flame. Your best policy now is to open the air entry ports wide. You need all the air you can get. With coaxing – and watching the growth of the fire profile into a longish shape – the blaze will slowly gather heat.

The next step is to close the upper, or flue, damper. Aha! you chortle. Another wood-burning scribe gone off his rocker! One instant he recommends more air. Now he advises cutting it off.

Bear with your wily, old woodwise writer and all shall be made clear. Wet wood demands stealthy cunning, as of Indians lying secretly in ambush. Wet wood has to be snuck up to and taken unawares.

You feed volumes of air through to it as a means of provoking a bit of an urge. Oh well! the wet wood murmurs. Might as well burn. Nothing much else happening.

So it burns a bit, and the meagre output of heat from this swirls up the chimney. Not good, that! Heat is for the hearth, house and home. So, you close the flue damper to the halfway position as a way of keeping some of this heat in.

Fooled by this manoeuvre, the wet wood starts to warm up inside the fire chamber, in spite of itself. As it warms, its wetness starts to evaporate and it settles down to the job of burning.

The fire makes progress. But you still have these mounds of wet wood in your log basket. These you now lay lovingly across the top of your stove. This is getting hotter by the minute. Steam from the wet wood shoots up. After a minute or so it is dry enough to go into the fire chamber.

This technique is so successful, that a cautionary word has to be introduced. Do not leave wet logs on top of the hot stove for too long. You will find, as I have, that they soon become dry enough to burst spontaneously into flame.

It does not need me to put down such self-evident items as not putting on your fire logs that are too large for it. The staying-in-overnight routine consists of no more than bunging the stove as full of reasonably-sized dry logs as it will take, shutting down all the dampers and letting the stove get on with it. If you have a back boiler feeding hot water to a tank and radiators by means of an electric pump, it does not need me to tell you to switch the pump off overnight to save money. I've already advised an annual chimney sweep as an antidote against tar.

There remains little more to be said. Those who faithfully follow these directives towards good wood fires will soon discover all that remains to be discovered for themselves, for in the final analysis every fire is as individual as the person running it.

Since writing this chapter, my policy of brisk burning has revealed a design defect in my Kamina stove that I must report.

While most of the fire chamber is composed of thin, cast-iron panels, there are ash guides at the bottom of each side of the burning area. These close the gap between the side wall and the bottom fire grate. The guides are made of thin, pressed steel. In my stove the left-hand guide has been distorted by the heat of the fire, so that a gap 11 centimetres long and 2 centimetres wide at its widest point has opened up along its top edge. This allows smoke to escape and ruins the draft control.

In fairness, the importers claim that this is the first case of this kind that they know about. It is suggested that the defect arose because in the factory, when the two components were assembled, they were fitted too tightly together, not allowing for expansion.

My own assessment, for what it is worth, is that the Belgian makers used steel plates for these parts as a way of cutting costs. They assumed that most of the time they would be covered by a thick layer of wood ash to protect them from the direct heat. My method of running the fire hot and clearing the ash regularly to improve the inflow of air has exposed the vulnerability of the design.

The importers say that on future models these steel plates will be replaced by cast-iron guides.

5

FREE FUEL FOR LIFE

Club members – as it might be, members of a wood-burning club – tend to find out about things from the inside. It was through an inner circuit of this kind that I discovered the work on which I was engaged was of national importance and vital to the survival of the realm. Suggesting that wood be burned as a fuel is hardly a novel idea. Man has been tossing logs into fires for aeons – perhaps, even longer than that. The notion that supplies of wood fuel can be guaranteed by replanting trees as they are cut down, however, must strike some of the international logging companies as an advanced novelty that needs a great deal of thinking about. All the same, the system works. Trees can be planted, and they actually grow. For various reasons, the best wood for burning is hard wood – the wood of deciduous, or broadleaf, trees – but hard wood trees tend to grow more slowly than soft wood conifers. To cope with the demand for hard woods (not only for burning) a good deal of research has been carried out on fast-growing hard woods. There you have a summary to date of the inside story.

In the course of one investigation for this volume, I found myself in contact with a corner of the Atomic Energy Research Establishment. One of its committees is compiling a review of alternative fuels. One of the commodities under scrutiny, and thereby, classified, it would seem, for administrative convenience as an atomic fuel – is wood. (The Americans do this kind of thing as well. Among President Carter's recently published list of solar fuels, you will find wood included.) The AERE committee is nothing if not thorough. Every last root and branch is being explored. To that end it has issued a contract to the Forestry Commission for the running of an

105

experimental fast-growing tree programme at the Alice Holt station, near Farnham, in Surrey. Because this work has been gathered under the general umbrella of atomic activity, again for administrative convenience, it has become classified as a kind of state secret. Whatever the explanation, I cannot find out anything about it.

Having reached this point, I settled back for further stocktaking. I mean, one knows what goes on. All the time we are assured by persons in authority that the only items to be given the secret classification are those of national importance and vital to the security of the realm.

Well, one is not daft. One can add two and two with the best of them. If wood growing is a secret then it must be of national importance. The security of the realm must in some way depend upon it.

There are potentially hostile (but unnamed) foreign powers whose agents are whirling in orbit above us, keeping a beady watch on what we do. The space-to-ground dialogue can be imagined. 'Great steaming samovars!' these agents mutter, peering out through the portholes of their space station. 'What are those dastardly British up to now? They are growing trees!'

The word goes whizzing back to the HQ of whatever organisation employs them, in the capital city of whichever nation is footing their bill, to the effect that the British are up to something pretty nasty in the tree-growing line and shouldn't this be written into the next SALT agreement!

Being an author in good standing and on the inside, one knows that when one door is closed another can be found open, with defective locks and a security guard who is turned 80, deaf and almost blind, who goes off duty at seven every evening and who is never there at weekends.

Quite by chance, however, there slipped into my hand a report on the global wood situation compiled by another organ of government than the previously mentioned AERE, the kind of thing that those agents of a foreign, hostile (but still unnamed) foreign power would dearly like to get their hands on. So too, I imagine, would the lads at the AERE.

This report has about it the look of a report that does not get around and about much. It is not actually stamped top secret, but there is a note on it stating that the work is for private information only and must not be cited in any publication.

Which is why I am about to cite it. Although I'm not going to indicate whose report it is, nor from which Quango it comes. For all I know they can still put you in the Tower for crimes of that kind!

What this report states is that, and I quote . . . I mean, the actual words it uses are . . . Oh dear! It doesn't look as if I shall be able to quote you a quote after all. It is written in such a thick, gobble-gunge prose that I doubt if even the agents of a foreign power could understand it. The general trend of its message is that, taking an investigative stomp around the world, wood supplies are found to be pretty much in balance with wood use. Trees are growing and being replanted, at just about the same rate they are being cut down. Some nations, like Japan, are buying up vast stretches of Asia and South America, and planting trees in those places as a hedge against future demand. The experience I have had myself with the tatty patch of woodland from which I take my timber is that here too growth is pretty much in line with consumption. Actually, now that summer is here, and I have to fight my way through a tangled mesh of slender young trees, I have the impression that growth may be ahead of cutting – although I may think differently again in the deeps of next winter. With that in mind, I am going to outline a scheme that will solve all your domestic fuel problems.

The plan, in a few words, is a programme to supply you with a virtually cost-free fuel supply for life. Many households now spend anything up to £1000 a year on centrally heating their homes, by fuel oil, natural gas or electricity and the costs of all these energy sources are going to rise. That is while supplies last. Eventually they will run down, peter out, fade away, vanish. 'Sold Out' is the sign that will appear round the world on all the fuel hoardings.

What I am about to suggest will commit you to an outlay of between one and two year's ordinary fuel costs. After that, virtually nothing. For ever.

Of course, as bit by bit I reveal the plan in all its stark simplicity, a number of hyper-active persons will rise to their feet and dash about the place putting the scheme into operation. Everyone else's options will narrow to that degree, and basic costs rise. All the same, at whatever stage of the ball game you decide to plunge in, the project is a nifty one – and, one of national importance, don't forget that.

The first move is to buy a plot of land. It makes little difference, in my experience, where you live and where you seek to buy land. The pattern varies little. If there is an established use for land, it is going to cost you. Land on which a home is to be built costs high. Land for agricultural use fetches, not such a stiff or steep whack, but sums well up to the dreams of avarice.

Between these lush patches of real estate there are to be found patchy parcels of unsellable land that no agent wants to handle because his profit will be too small. What I am talking about is land that cannot be used for building or growing crops – scrub woodland.

You find plots of scrub woodland everywhere that trees grow. Nobody wants them. Maybe there will be a clump of trees in the gulley between two fields on a farm; the farmer cannot get his machines into them. Or, there will be a stretch of neglected woodland on an old family estate; there is no longer enough money to employ a forester. The trees are not commercially valuable enough to cover the cost of cutting them down. So, they are just left to grow in their rough, unkempt natural style, entangling themselves more intricately with every year that trudges past. For commercial use the trees are too large, or too small, or the undergrowth is too thick to cut through. You don't care about any of these things. For you only one point counts – it will all burn.

Suppose round a bend in a lane you come across a tangle of trees, oak, let us imagine. At the density likely to result from natural regeneration – old trees dying when their time comes, and acorns plunging to the ground each season and taking root therein – the quantity of standing timber in the woodland will be something of the order of – wait for it! – 100 tonnes per acre. Natural growth will add to that an average of one tonne of new

108

wood per acre each year. It has been calculated that five tonnes of hard wood will centrally heat a three-bedroom house for a year. Five acres of scrub woodland will, therefore, supply enough fuel to keep you (and your family) warm for as long as the woodland stands. All you have to do is find – and buy – the five acres, as specified. Not easy, but not impossible.

There is no certain road to this purchase. Just because you bought a copy of this book and are reading these words, don't imagine you will be able to reach out and grab hold of a five acre parcel just like that. Especially at the right price, which is the price I am recommending, namely something between one and two year's ordinary central heating fuel cost.

If everybody who could, did this, enough pressure would be removed from the fuel oil market to enable us to get through the next few winters without too much difficulty. The shortfall in oil supply is currently about 4 per cent. And there is enough timber standing to supply about 5 per cent of the domestic fuel market, ultimately, with a bit more national organisation, perhaps even 10 per cent could be wood fuelled.

How are you going to latch on to these five acres? Scan the auction announcements of as many local, rural newspapers as you can gather in. Study the sales of farmland and estates. Go and have a look at some of them. If there are likely bits of woodland, attend the auction. A chap who has just laid out several hundred thousand on a few hundred acres might be glad to recoup a thousand cash down on a patch of land that will never be any use to him.

Cruise through country districts. If you see a likely knob of trees, knock on a few local doors to find who owns them. This is not so extreme a suggestion as you might think. In rural districts, people are used to this approach. Often it is the only way of finding out who owns what. The local authorities are not able to help very often. They keep no record of land ownership. Their only records relate to dwellings for rating demands. Land is not rateable and slips through their net.

If the land is owned by a local chap, knock on his door, and wave a (metaphorical) fistful of notes in his face. He may be so overwhelmed with surprise that he will bite on your offer. If land is owned by a syndicate or company, find out their address, or that of their solicitor, and bung in a letter. It is often amazing how a firm cash offer for something previously judged worthless will flush out a yes-vote.

This may all take time – but the reward is worth it. And remember, it *is* work of national importance.

You will note I have carefully avoided spelling out the sort of price you should pay, except as a relationship to what is now being skimmed from your coffers by the oil, gas and electrical lads. Suppose your present heating bill is £1000 a year – and my suggestion is for a five acre price of between one and two years heating costs, then something between £200 and £400 per acre would be within this. Sounds hyper-low, I know, but I've recently (in 1979) known land to change hands at prices well within that.

If, by the time you get round to reading this book, your fuel costs have gone up, presumably these scrub land prices will have risen by the same degree. Meantime, other persons will have also read the book and got in the market, which will shove the price up a bit more. All the same, once you've got the conveyance in your hot little hand, you can pretty well say good-bye to inflation-puffed fuel price rises.

Naturally, those agents of foreign powers (there is bound to be more than one) will do their best to spike this programme by passing the word round that what is going to happen is the outbreak of a night-of-the-long-knives, resulting in the levelling of all trees, reducing the realm to the status of a treeless desert. Stuff your ears against this drivel and read on.

If you see in your handy gardening magazine that fruit bushes need to be pruned hard back this month, you do not instantly head for the wailing wall to bemoan the end of all fruit bushes as we have known them. Pruning, you know, is a process that gives the fruit bush the necessary get up and go to see it through another hectic season of busy fruit bushing resulting in lush plantations of fruit bursting forth. Trees are just a step up from fruit bushes, with very much the same kind of tastes, life-style and inclinations. Trim or cut back your average tree and this is enough to encourage it to produce a few more branches.

Sensible tree management, applied to neglected woodland, centres on the cutting out each year of the same amount of dead wood as is produced by new growth. This will result in the trees growing more rapidly and healthily than before.

For the keener, more energetic and rugged souls I am honour-bound to mention that there is an even longer and harder road available for you to tread to this Elysian goal. You can, if you are so minded, buy a piece of bare land, clear it and plant your own trees. Of course, if it is hard persuading some land owning baron to part with a piece of worthless scrub woodland, it is going to be even harder to get the bite on the self-same l.o.b. to the tune of a few bare acres on which, at the moment of your application, he assumes you intend to build a luxury hotel, high-rise deluxe flatlets or some other similarly profitable enterprise, and has visions of doing the same thing himself. However, if the land is rough enough and remote enough it is not impossible that you can acquire it for some kind of song. Against this song you will have to weigh in the cost scales what you are going to have to pay to prepare the land and plant in it trees where no trees grew before. I mean, trees don't grow on trees, you know. They cost. After the clearing, seedlings have to be planted at a density of perhaps 1000 to the acre, and thinned out when they mature. Each seedling may cost you up to £1.00. And you'd have to hang about for a minimum of 10 years before you could get in there with your trusty saw and cut into the wood supplies.

Still, as a plan, it is workable and should be mentioned. If you have the eyes-on-the-distant-horizon, visionary approach to life, this might be something for you to have a stab at.

However, if this turns out to be your thing, do not look to me for expert help and guidance. I am no forester and this is not a practical treatise on forestry. Expect only of me that I may be able to fill you in on the more salient features. For the rest, skilled directions are available in an excellent series of handbooks published by the Forestry Commission and available from branches of Her Majesty's Stationery Office, or their agents. Sectional List No. 31 gives details of the various bulletins, booklets, forest records, leaflets and reports available. Here are a few that I can recommend:

Silviculture Bulletins: No. 14, Forestry Practice; No. 43, Nursery Practice; No. 55, Aspects of Thinning. Forest Records: No. 113, Free Growth of Oak. Leaflets: No. 61, Tubed Seedlings.
Management and Measurement Booklets: No. 32, Thinning Control in British Woodlands; No. 46, Management of Small Woodlands.

In addition, a chat with any Forestry Commission person in your district would also dredge up a wealth of practical information. It might also dredge up some cash. For tree planting programmes with a minimum area of 0·6 of a hectare, there are cash grants available.

Having told you all that, I think I have done about as much for you as I can. As I explained at the start of the book, I prefer wherever possible to keep within the bounds of things I have worked at and done myself. Theorists are all too thick on the ground. And my own limits are the grubbings about on a trial and error basis (mostly the latter) that I have stumbled through in neglected woodlands. So, this is the safer ground to which I intend to return now.

Back to this scramble of trees that is going to be the exclusive source of household heat for you from now on. As you cast your eyes across it for the first time, one of the thoughts that may come to you is the quantity of burnable stuff just lying about on the ground. Waste is a terrible thing anyway, but when it strikes at your own domestic creature comforts it makes your soul ache. Something, you feel, simply must be done, and you resolve, with one of those firmer, inner, passionate resolves that we all have when the balance of our minds is disturbed: You will pick up, you tell yourself, gather in, store and make use of all those bits of wood on the ground and turn them into worthwhile heat. Believe me, don't kid yourself. It will never happen.

What you propose is what economic chaps call labour intensive. That means, it is going to entail a great deal of personal back-breaking, and there are no machines available to help you. Let me outline the problem. The ground cover in mixed woodland consists of wood pieces, twigs, scraps of bark, bits of root, fallen leaves and other vegetation. With time these all congeal into a thick, woody, peaty mass that burns quite well. But, how do you pick it up? The woody fibres are so tough and springy that you can't cut through them with the blade of a shovel and so lift a load. The only practical thing is to get down on your hands and knees and scrabble it up piece by piece, but your fire will race through the clumps faster than you can pick them up.

Assuming you have already gathered in a supply, where are you going to keep it? These mixtures of wood bits are not cohesive. They don't hang together. Put them in a heap and before long, you will be tramping knee-deep through wood crumbs all over the house. One possible way might be to pack them into small plastic bags of the kind you use to store food in your kitchen fridge. Again, it is expensive and time consuming.

If we assume again that all these hurdles have been overcome, how do you put this fuel on your fire? You can bung it on one bag at a time. Whoosh! and the bag is gone. Or, if you try putting it on in handfuls, you would have to squat there all day, working as fast as you could to keep the fire in business.

So, despite the fact that this fuel reserve, lying about, and cluttering up your newly acquired woodland, scales out at anything up to a kilo of material to the square metre – say, an average of two tonnes to the acre (five tonnes to the hectare) – you are going to have to let it lie there, no matter how much this bruises your finer feelings. It simply is not worth the scratch.

There is, perhaps, an industrial way of sorting this out. It is a process called briquetting, but it is too long and complex to deal with here. I will return to it in Chapter 7. For the moment, let us stick strictly to what you can do for yourself.

Moving up the wood scale, the next commodity you will find in the woods is a galaxy of burnable items also lying on the ground. Some are branches brought down by high winds, or the remains of trees that have become old, diseased and have died.

Whether or not you can burn these depends on how long the wood has been lying on the ground. If it has lain there for no more than a year there will still be sufficient resin in the fibre to prevent water soaking into the heartwood. Only the exterior and first layers will be wet. These can be quickly air dried.

Possibly the wood has been on the ground for two or more years, in which case a degree of rot will have set in. You can always tell. First, there is the characteristic sweet, sickly smell of decayed wood. The timber itself will have started flaking on the surface. In extreme cases, there will be such an advanced degree of wood crumble that it will disintegrate into fragments when you try to lift it from the ground. In which case, forget it.

But otherwise, cull your rotten wood with care. It burns well and provides a useful source of heat while you are getting your main supplies organised. Be careful not to store rotted wood adjacent to good wood. The rot can spread.

So here we are, hands on hips, surveying with rising optimism this work of national importance that you are about to undertake. As with all such work, there has to be a five-year plan. The Russians, who have had more five-year plans than most of us have had hot summers, always have a five-year plan tucked away in reserve to cope with every contingency. They began their revolution with a five-year plan based on an acre and a cow for every family. Our five-year plan cancels the cow and adds another four acres to the first. So, here we go with the start of year one.

The first task is to establish a supply chain of wood from where it grows to the stove where it will be burned. My experience suggests that this be done in stages for at least the first year.

The key to all successful wood burning is the percentage of water in the wood. Freshly cut, green, wood has up to 50 per cent of moisture. This has to be got rid of, which is going to take a minimum of six months of air drying. Meanwhile, you have to find something your fire can get its teeth into.

The sensible way is to work through your woodland in stages. Don't just thrash around. Mark the area out in roughly equal divisions. You can make each one the area you will clear in a day. Or, you can work to larger sections that will occupy you for a week. I prefer the last arrangement, principally because you don't see everything at once. You drag, tug, lug

A tumble stack

and haul every scrap of moveable timber from a patch – the next day you go back and see masses that you overlooked the first time. So, weekly divisions are best. Nor am I suggesting that you make these formal divisions. Map out the sections roughly by eye – today you will work up to that bush, and you will have everything cleared up to the ditch by the end of the week. Something of that kind. Only, don't forget where you are working in any one week. Once you are muddled it takes a bit of careful organisation to get you straight again.

We will imagine your situation to be that the cold weather will soon be upon you and fires will be required. To start with you have no reserves of wood whatever. You start with nothing.

You need a working and storage area, preferably under some kind of minimal cover. As I have said, a large car port is very suitable. You begin by dragging in from the weekly sections you have marked with your eye. At first you will only be able to tumble-stack these in a loose jumble – this occupies much space. Probably you won't get it all under cover.

This is not of such vital importance as you might imagine. Even if rain falls on it, the wood will dry out quite swiftly when the rain stops. If the wood is already fairly dry, rain damp won't penetrate. If the wood is already wet, rain will hardly make it significantly wetter.

What you now have to do is make the wood more capable of

115

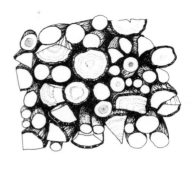

(left) A cord of logs and *(right)* logs locked together to form a firm stack

being dried. And it must be cut to the size of your stove. This kills those two birds with the one saw cut. The short lengths of wood, stacked so that air can circulate through them, will shed their moisture more readily, and can then go straight into your stove's fire chamber.

You begin to develop a daily routine – not a lengthy, time-consuming one, but fitting in with whatever allowance of time you can make. Each day you spend some time bringing in wood. You follow this with a session of sawing. (I will deal with the techniques of breaking down wood later on.)

Gradually in some outside place – under the car port or in a shed or outhouse, you will build up a small supply of logs – perhaps as much as a week's supply.

Just in case your other, or better, half is keeping a watchful eye on your activities, let me pop in here the firm recommendation that you provide yourself with a set of very old clothes and a pair of decent leather gardening gloves. You will be very surprised how messy wet, decayed wood is, and at the weird variety of stains it will leave on your clothes. Your hands will be scratched and torn by bark, splinters and thorns if not protected. Also, in winter, they get very cold.

While we are on the subject of equipment, let me deal with saws. I find that the best saw is the *smallest* bow saw with which you are comfortable. For my own use I have the smallest

Swedish Sandvik 21-inch model, which is easily portable, comfortable to work with and will quickly saw through wood up to a diameter of 15 centimetres (6 inches) which is about the maximum size you will generally handle, at least to start with.

Finally, a cheap pair of sturdy boots – not rubber pull-on wellies. Buy extra long football boot laces – and tie these, not only on top of the boot as usual, but run them also under the boot instep and lace them there as well. This may result in muddy laces, but it will give you the firmest possible foothold. As you stumble about in wet and slippery woodland, you must keep your footing. Often you will find yourself contorted into a double-jointed posture so as to give your saw blade a good purchase on an awkwardly placed log. At any time after you have cut halfway through, the log may suddenly collapse, give way, come apart in a shower of splintery bits, issuing, as it does so, a loud, disagreeable 'crack'. If you slip just then, you might easily get a heavy load of wood descending on your person with unpleasant results. Don't brood about this. Care will keep you clear. I am the most cack-footed of persons and it has never happened to me. But, just watch it!

Sooner or later I will have to raise the question of chain saws. I might as well do it now. It is likely to be the last time you see it mentioned in this book. I don't like chain saws. I have a deep-rooted prejudice against them, based on fear. To be blunt, they scare me hollow. I listen to the professional tree fellers talking and hear of the horrendous happenings they have with these damaging instruments, and I feel more and more strongly that these are not for me. Nothing now would persuade me to use one. Whether my attitude will change, I don't know. Everyone assumes that as you get older and less able to cope with physical stress, you tend to turn to machines for help. If I grow old and decrepit and unable to carry on my daily sawing work load, it is supposed that going over to chain sawing will be the answer. I am not convinced of this. If I cannot handle a small, light bow saw, how would I be able to handle a buzzing, thrusting, leaping chain saw which is heavier to lift and harder to control?

But, I emphasise, this is a personal attitude. For you it may be different. Perhaps you can control machinery better than I can. Perhaps, if you have no fear of these machines, they will be as putty in your hands. This is an age of mechanisation and it is easy to be tempted by the sales ads. If you are, then I can only repeat that chain saws are dangerous instruments, but useful. If you want to use one, let me quote the Forestry Commission recommendations to their own professional chaps:

Boots: A safety toe cap is essential. Canadian lumber boots with a rubber foot and leather upper are best.
Gloves: Left-hand mitts and right-hand mitts with the index finger in waterproofed leather are required for chain saw work.
Hard hats: These are essential if you are bringing down branches.
Eye nets: Wire gauze with a plastic surround, and designed to attach to the hard hat, these are essential for chain saw work (to prevent wood bits flying into your eye).
Ear muffs: Essential for work with chain saws. Ear plugs are not recommended.

Ballistic nylon material is available which will resist the cutting action of a chain saw until the chain stops. It should be specified for chain saw gloves – on the back of the left hand and thumb.

If you remain convinced that a chain saw – either a portable petrol driven model, or an electric one that will plug in, usefully, under your car port sawing area – will make the wood-cutting operation more practicable for you, then the best of British. But, I've worked for a year now with nothing more lethal than a small bow saw, a $4\frac{1}{2}$ pound axe, a hammer and a pair of wedges. And I've hardly got a bruise to show for it. My wood is piled up in neat stacks, the exercise keeps me fit and my weight down and I am still here telling you my tale.

Now, back to the wood itself. I will suppose we have got you organised with wood supplies coming in, a work area arranged, under cover if possible, and equipped with a small saw horse, and in one corner a stack of logs cut to length is gradually building up.

Although I have this bug against mechanisation, I suppose I could concede that a wheelbarrow can be handy. Don't get one that is too large. Don't overstrain yourself. Stick to what you can lift comfortably. There is always time for a second trip.

If the woodland is some distance from your house, I might also acknowledge that it could be helpful to have a small trailer that can be attached to the back of your car, or buy a clapped-out mini-van. As it won't have to run great distances, it doesn't have to be in particularly good condition – just good enough to get it through the MOT test!

The time has come to talk of grading your wood, probably into three sizes. You want big wood to burn on the fire, nice chunky lumps of wood, loggy lengths that will burn for an hour or so. If you are using a closed, airtight stove, check beforehand the maximum size of wood that will go through the loading door. Sometimes I have cut a piece to the right length and then found it was too thick to go through the door. Very frustrating on a chilly night. This may mean that you have to trim off awkward knobs of wood, or short stubs of branch that project at a difficult angle. At least make sure that everything that is stacked ready for burning will go in.

Following the large size, you will require medium pieces, something between chunks and twigs. These are useful in two ways. First, they help to get the fire going in its early stages when large pieces would simply not take flame. Second, during continuous firing, it is helpful to have a mix of wood sizes for each loading to assist in transfering the flaming heat of the burning wood to the new stuff and so keep up a steady output of heat.

Finally, you will need twigs as kindling – very small, thin pieces with which to start your fire.

Under the car port, or wherever you are storing your wood, the large and medium pieces can be piled in the same stack. Twigs and kindling wood are best kept separate. They are too springy to lock into a wood pile, and may cause it to come apart and topple over. Make sure, incidentally, that each piece of wood locks into place with the other pieces around it. There is nothing worse than a loose pile. When you have several layers piled, weight will help to keep the pile solid and stable.

We have now moved your wood from the tree growing area to the place where it is being stored. It has been cut to size and stacked. What is the next link in the chain of fuel supply?

For that we must shift inside. My suggestion is a large, sturdy wood box large enough to contain two to three days of wood supplies. Remember that this is your first year of burning and that you are fighting to remove enough water from the wood to make it burnable. If you are able to give the cut logs a minimum of a week's drying in the open air under a car port, or something similar, then moving it indoors will give it a final drying boost, and make sure it stays dry. In addition to which, on dark, frosty nights, you do not want to be making frequent trips outside to fetch in more supplies. You need to be kept dry and warm as well!

The wood box indoors satisfies all these needs – but you may have to rearrange things to find a place to keep it. My own box is just under 5 feet long, 2 feet across and about 18 inches high. Placed just inside the front door it also acts as a convenient seat for people to plump down on, to change wet shoes on rainy days. This is big enough to take three piles of wood, each pile lasts me about a day.

Even that isn't the end of my line. I am lazy and I don't enjoy having to leave the fireside to fetch in wood, even from the wood box. And there is still the chance to achieve more in the way of drying. The fire, once alight, throws out quantities of direct heat. To take advantage of this, I have another container, a wood basket, beside the fire. In this I pile an evening's load. The warmth from the fire helps to drive out the last whisps of moisture so that the logs, when they finally are flung into the fire, flame and spurt with merry energy.

So, there we have all the stages – the timber is pulled, carted, wheelbarrowed or mini-vanned in from the woods. It is cut to size and stacked. A saw cut across the top of the saw horse will help to control cutting the wood in accurate lengths. Two to five inches in diameter is classed as large wood; one to two inches as medium. Anything smaller is for kindling. From the outside store, the wood is moved to the wood box inside, and from there to the fireside basket. Each of these moves is made daily. You bring in enough branches to keep up your supply. You saw enough to keep the stack the same size or larger. You pile the newly cut wood on one end, and remove dry wood from the other end. Each day you bring in enough wood to top up the fire box, and every evening you make sure your fireside basket is full.

It sounds a lot of labour and yet it isn't. I estimate that on average I spend about a total of an hour each day working my wood. Some days it is rather more, other days it is less. Each week I give myself a day off with no wood work whatever.

The effect of this programme on your woodland after the first full winter is that you will have cleared most of the lying timber. The tree patch will begin to perk up with all the attention it is receiving.

The next step is to begin to cut out the dead trees. There will be a surprising number. You don't notice them during the winter when all the trees look dead anyway. But in the spring the sap starts to flow again in the live trees, buds appear and leaves open. That is when you can spot the dead ones. They stand there just as starkly leafless as in winter. If you are expert at it, you can tell which trees are alive even in winter. You scratch the bark with your nail, if it is horny enough, or with a small nailfile if it is not. If the tree is alive, the white wood under the bark will be moist with sap. If the wood is dry, it is probably dead. However, the distinction between live and dead trees is not so absolute as that. Often, you will discover that a tree is dead from a certain height upwards, but is still alive lower down. If you cut down the dead part along the dividing line, as it were, this will encourage fresh growth from the lower limbs.

There is no argument against removing dead trees. Once a tree is dead, it will do nothing for your woodland except act as a focus for disease and decay. There is every argument in favour of removing the dead ones. They burn well and they give growing room for the living trees. In a woodland or forest, the impetus that drives trees to grow upwards with the greatest vigour is the vital need to capture their share of sunshine on the surface of their leaves. The trees that achieve this, flourish and spread. Those that lose out in this race remain stunted, and will eventually die. Cutting the dead ones out encourages the more vital trees to do even better. This has the effect of thickening

121

your woodland growth and extending tree cover over a greater area. By cutting out old wood for fuel, you are laying down your supplies for the future.

When you reach this stage, at the start of your second year perhaps, you can begin to modify your chain of wood supply. Because, not only will you be removing dead trees, but sooner or later you will begin to make decisions about the still living trees. These have to be thinned and coppiced also.

I have already given you an indication as to what coppicing is. Almost any broad leaf tree, when cut down to a stump, will grow again. (Living trees should be cut only between October and March when the sap is down. Otherwise the wood will be too wet, and tree growth may not regenerate). Buds and shoots will appear from the live bark and these grow up around the old stump, like a crown. After a number of years, these will, in turn, be thick enough for you to cut again as fuel. Trees can be coppiced up to eight or nine times before they grow too old, lose their vigour and will coppice no longer. It depends on the species of tree and its speed of growth what rotation of coppicing you will adopt, but something around a 15 year interval is the most likely.

But all that is for the future. For the present, it is likely that taking out the dead trees will satisfy all your fuel needs in the second year of your woodland saga.

By the third year, it is my guess you will be ready to start work on live wood. Cries of horror and hands flung skywards in disgust! Cut down live trees! Never!

Hold hard, maties! When you dig your spuds from the ground, are they not live? Or your pea pods, fresh runner beans, tomatoes, lettuce? That's different, you respond. That is what they are grown for.

What I'm suggesting is that you grow your wood for just as sensible a reason. And being sensible, you do not hack about like a mad thing, but in accord with a rational plan that is, at least in part, based on the natural needs of the trees themselves. In wild woods, seeds fall from the mature trees each year. Some germinate, take root and grow. The result is that without some orderly control you get a large mass of thin, spindly trees all competing with each other for nutrients in the soil, and for the vital sunlight that flickers through the leaves of older trees above.

They can't all make it. Nature is ruthless and hard. Some will thrive, others will die and a large middle group will hover in some silvicultural never-never land, neither doing very well, nor doing badly enough to fade away. You have to make some of nature's decisions for her – or rather, you have to speed them up a bit. These thin, weedy trees will never grow great guns. Nature will pull them down eventually. You merely advance matters by a season or two.

This will be a theoretical consideration to you now, sitting comfortably reading these words. If you disagree, hold back your final decision until you have tried to fight your way through thick growths of these spindle-shank trees, their twisty stems and branches plucking at your clothes and skin, flicking blindingly at your eyes, twisting your feet from under you. Then my argument will strike you with a little more force.

All the same, it is a hard decision to make – not on sentimental, but practical grounds. By careful study and observation, you have to make up your mind which trees will grow the best, and which should be removed to give them growing room.

Cutting live green wood, by now must modify your stacking programme. During all those months, both summer and winter, from your first to your third year of wood fuelling, you have been steadily cutting and stacking, building up reserves. You become squirrel-like in your attitudes. No longer do you see pleasant trees and woodland. All you notice are present and potential wood supplies. A branch seen lying on the ground will cause you to ache with longing to pick it up.

The stack under the car port will have grown to a monumental edifice of mixed woods and sizes, all cut to the required length. You continue cutting through the summer to buttress the household against the chill days of winter. So that now, the minimum air-drying period of six months for green wood is something well within your grasp. Probably, if you have continued to cut and saw steadily, you will be able to manage a full year of storage before the wood is burned.

In this third year of the programme, the trees I suggest you cut down are those with a diameter at knee height of no more than six to eight inches. (The same size limitation applies to the dead trees you cut down in the second year.) Anything larger is best dealt with by a professional tree feller.

But cutting trees of this size, no matter what height they have, is not so difficult as you might imagine. Of course, you must be careful and plan each cutting operation beforehand. But, you still need only the small trusty 21-inch bow saw.

Depending on the tree's situation and what surrounds it, you have to plan at what height to cut it and from what angle. Usually, this is self-evident. You cut from whatever angle you can best reach the tree. But you need also to observe the way the tree is growing, if there is a slant to it, and the way it will fall.

The two vital, but simple precautions are: you do not want the tree to fall on you, and you don't want the butt of the tree, where you have made the cut, to strike back as the tree falls, and catch you an unexpected cropper.

Suppose the tree is a thick eight inches. This will seem more massive than it really is. Do not be deterred.

Start sawing at the best height and angle. At first your tiny saw will seem to be making little impression. But keep at it and within about two minutes (if you have a decent blade – bow saw blades should be replaced when you can feel the wood gripping the blade as it cuts – this means the saw teeth that are set to make a cut through the wood that is larger than the saw blade thickness, have now worn so that the cut is the same thickness as the blade) you will have cut about a third of the way into the trunk or bole.

Now move round the tree and continue cutting from a different angle, but extending the same cut sideways. If the surrounding undergrowth will allow it, continue this sideways extension of the cut in both directions.

There are two reasons for doing this. A saw blade cuts best along a narrow neck of wood, because it has less binding friction to overcome from the wood itself. If you continue cutting across the full thickness of the trunk, not only will the

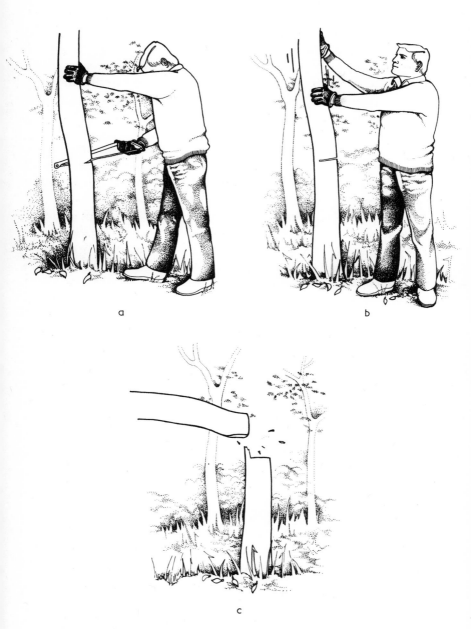

Taking down a tree: (a) the saw cut; (b) rocking the trunk; (c) the tree falls along the chosen line

bow-saw frame be thumping against the wood, restricting blade movement, but at least half your effort will be going into overcoming wood friction.

The second reason is that you want to arrive at a point where the tree is supported on a slender corner of uncut wood, on the side away from you, and in the direction towards which you want the tree to fall.

When you reach that point, stop and have a think. Is the tree cutting going according to your original plan? In which case, are you standing in the right position? What will happen when the tree falls? What other trees or obstructions will it fall on? In which direction will the bottom of the tree trunk kick back when it falls? Will you be in the line of fire? If it does something unexpected can you jump out of the way quickly? Is there anything on the ground that may catch your feet and cause you to stumble and fall? In other words, have a good hard look all round the situation.

If it should happen that someone has come along to lend you a hand or supply moral support to your tree cutting exercise, make sure before the tree goes down that they are standing at least *twice the height* of the tree distant from you. This may sound an extreme precaution, but it is advice given me by the Forestry Commission. When trees are going down, they tell me, the most surprising things can sometimes happen, and it is best to be on the safe side.

Then, place your hand against the trunk a short way above the cut you have made, and start to rock it gently. At first, if the tree is thick and heavy (and remember, about a third or a quarter of the trunk remains to be cut through) there will be hardly any movement. But build up a gentle rhythm. It doesn't take much effort – just careful timing, so that you apply your push each time the tree reaches the end of its rock at your end. Gradually, you will build up a regular, steady oscillation, which you continue to increase until you hear the first faint crack. That means the tree is ready to go. Now, when the tree rocks away from you, you hold it with your hand, so that it can't rock back towards you. (Or you can use a wedge to hold it, but that is slightly more awkward.)

126

The tree is now balanced, poised, ready to fall. Have another good look all round to make sure all is clear. Then apply a steady pressure away from you. The tree will begin to go down. You can see the movement of the trunk and you can hear the wood cracking across the uncut part on the far side of the trunk from you. At this instant, step back away from the tree, a good six feet at least. Let the tree go down on its own – and don't go near it again until you are quite sure it has done all the falling it is going to do.

Now you have a large lump of tree lying on the ground, and you have to cut it into transportable sections. First, you must judge for yourself what weight of wood you can comfortably carry. Don't try to lift too much. The load that seems easy to lift for five seconds, weighs a ton when you have heaved it about 20 yards.

Trim away the smaller branches, then do a few test lifts on what remains to see how heavy it is. Decide on a section to cut, and get stuck in with your trusty saw. It is important to have some kind of support just under where you are cutting, or very close to it. Otherwise, as you saw deeper into the wood, the weight remaining on either side will cause the trunk to sag, so closing up your saw cut, and binding the saw blade so that you cannot move it. This can also happen when you are cutting the tree as it stands. It can be remedied by leaning one hand against the trunk as you saw with the other. It may sound tricky, but you won't have to do it for more than a few cuts. By then the depth of your cut and the weight of the tree as it tries to fall, will be pulling the cut open again.

All that remains now is to hump the wood, one length at a time, on to your shoulder, into your wheelbarrow or whatever transport you have, and get it back to your sawing and stacking area.

This cutting programme will continue into the fourth year of this Master Wood Fuel Plan, by which time you should be able to see the possibility of clearing one or two areas completely. The time is now ripe for replanting – either seeds or seedlings. I am not going to describe that procedure or recommend species of tree. I'm not an expert and I don't know enough about it. In

127

any case, the Forestry Commission handbooks I have already recommended will give you all the detailed information you want. If you buy in your seedling trees from a nursery man, he too should be able to direct your efforts.

There remains only to mention the task for your fifth year. That is to make a long-term rotational plan for your woods. If you are going to work to a 10 to 15 year rotation, then make a detailed assessment which trees you are going to cull, and when. Probably, if you have any very large old trees, it will be best to leave these standing. They will provide wind protection for your younger trees (and some frost protection in winter also) and maintain a general shape for your woodland as a whole.

By these labours you will provide your house with year-round fuel, keep yourself healthy, supply the atmosphere with oxygen, sustain the woodland amenity for the environment, protect the safety of the realm and do work of vital national importance!

6

WOODS AND ENDS

Joining a club is fine, but there comes one day the moment of grim reality, when you rise from your prone telly position and venture forth to cut wood. Yet, when you get right into it, you actually get a taste for the rhythms of the saw and axe. None of it turns out to be as bad as non-wood-stove-burning critics make out.

A modicum of equipment is enough to get the enthusiast into play. One sawing horse, an axe and a saw will do the trick.

A sawing horse can be knocked up by almost any DIY handy person. A balk of timber 1 metre long (39 inches), 15 centimetres wide (6 inches), and 5 centimetres thick (2 inches) will start you off. To this must be added at each end, a pair of legs, splayed out to form an inverted V. The height above ground will vary according to individual taste, but I find about 48 centimetres (19 inches) is just about right. I'll explain why in an instant.

It is useful to measure the length of log you are going to cut along the top of the horse and mark this with a cut deep enough for you to recognise when the top is half-clogged with saw dust. In my case I have two cuts: a longish one, which measures the maximum length of log I can use in my enclosed Kamina stove and in my open Jetmaster grate (as it happens, these are the same length) and a shorter length of wood to use in my baby Trolla.

Trees are inconvenient in that they do not all grow to a standard size. You have to deal with them as they come. But we will assume here that however oddly shaped your wood is, it is no more than 15 centimetres (6 inches) in diameter. In other words, it is of a size that your small bow saw — you will

The sawing horse; note the cuts to mark log lengths

remember that earlier I recommended the 53-centimetre (21-inch) size – can cut through using direct cuts.

Suppose you are dealing with a small tree just as it has come from the ground, 15 centimetres in diameter at the base, with roots attached, and tapering along its length of 10 metres to about two centimetres. (Such a tree will weigh between 20 and 25 kilos and can easily be carried by one person, balanced on the shoulder.)

The first task is to remove the roots by cutting across the base of the trunk. (The roots can be trimmed to size later – they will burn quite well.)

There are two basic sawing techniques. The philosophy is this: you are working with a frail human body, none of the individual parts of which is particularly strong. Therefore, the policy is to bring as many of them to bear on the task in hand, working in combination.

Having cut away the roots, you lay the tree along the top of the sawing horse with the cut end beside your sawing hand – depending on whether you are right or left handed. You edge the tree trunk along so that the end is lined up with the end of the horse. Make a cut above the mark on the horse showing the length of log you are going to produce. Move the trunk along so that the cutting mark is now dangling about five centimetres or so *beyond* the top of the horse – this is so your saw does not bite down into your valuable piece of equipment.

If you are right handed – I am, and all subsequent descriptions will be for right-handed people; left-handed bods should just turn every action the other way around – you will probably grasp the trunk with your left hand to steady it, and saw with your right.

After a while a defect in your human body will show up. You will discover an ache developing in the muscles of your right (sawing) arm, and a strong inclination develop to down tools and toddle off for coffee. The way round this is to bring more body parts into play. Lift the left leg – and here the height of the sawing horse becomes critical – and thump it down to hold the trunk in place. If possible, rotate the log so that any projecting

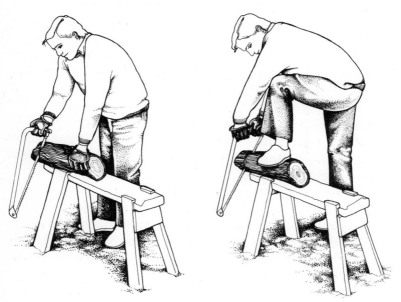

(*left*) A poor sawing method and (*right*) a better way

131

stumps will lock against the top of the sawing horse so that your weight holds the wood firm.

You can now reach across with your left hand and grasp the saw handle with both hands. Using the power of your shoulders and getting as far across on top of the cutting action as possible, you will find the additional weight and power of your cutting stroke will whizz you through the wood in double short time, and with less of that nagging arm ache. The full length of tree will slide through your hands and, before you know it, a neat and stackable pile of logs will reward your efforts.

But trees are awkward things, never willing to co-operate with the wood-cutting person in a way that he might feel justified to expect. For one thing, they never grow to the wanted size, being too small when something larger is wanted, and vice versa. And speaking of this, sooner rather than later, a trunk will come along that is bigger than the recommended 15 centimetres. It may even swell to a daunting 20 or 25 centimetres. The direct cutting approach will no longer work. Before you are even half-way through, the frame of your bow saw will be bobbing about the top side of the tree trunk. Soon there will no longer be enough freedom of movement for sawing to continue.

There is a way round this: tackle the trunk from the most convenient angle and cut into it to about a third of the total thickness. Next, rotate the trunk so that you are now cutting across the top end of the first cut. Again, continue to cut through to about a third of the trunk's depth. Rotate again and repeat the manoeuvre. You now have a cut that goes right round the circumference of the tree trunk. Continue cutting and rotating. Eventually you will win through and the mighty balk that seemed impregnable, will fall at your feet, an easy victim to your deadly cutting action.

However, having cut such a monster down to length, it is still likely that its thickness will prevent you shoving it straight on your fire. Further reductions are necessary and these you will perform with an axe.

First, the instrument: you will need a hefty, well-made axe with a head weighing about 2 kilos (4½ pounds). If you have a

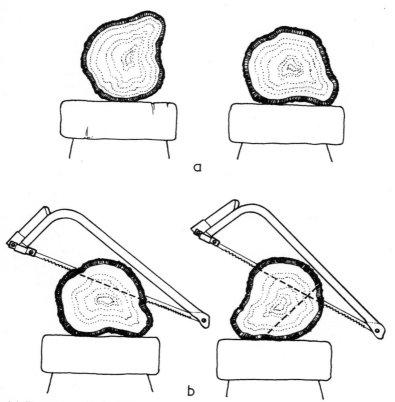

(a) Rotating to lock the log; (b) rotating the log to improve the saw cut

large lump of tree trunk to form a chopping block, that will help, but it is not essential.

The first thing is to decide where to cut. Study the piece of wood in question. How does the grain run? Does it seem – so far as you can judge – that the grain runs reasonably straight throughout the length of wood? If so, balance the trunk upright. Stand well back, feet apart, at the right distance for the axe to come whanging down on the centre of the upright log. Swing the axe above your head, judge the distance, and mark a point across the centre of the log top as your aiming point. You won't hit it more than once in ten shots, but never mind. Put all your weight behind the swing and flash it down. If you hit the right

The axe chop

spot – and the wood is fairly dry – the axe will cleave down through the wood, splitting it asunder along its length with a most satisfying coming-apart kind of noise. It may be that a few tough old fibres refuse to let go. You can pull these apart with your bare hands.

 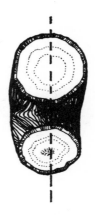 

Splitting a Y-section stump

It may happen that you thwack down as hard as you can on a length of wood with your axe and get little joy by way of penetration. What you then have to discover is the natural line of cleavage. Turn the log through 90 degrees and try again. If you still have no luck, try again at the other end. If the wood has dried and small cracks , radiating from the central heartwood, have begun to appear, these may indicate the line along which you should chop. Sooner or later, you'll find a way to make the wood submit.

If you have a length of wood for splitting that still has a stump of branch attached, this poses a problem. It is like trying to cut through a knot. The fibrous mass of tissue in the cleft between the main stem and the branch resists the axe: the blade just bounces back. One solution is to chop down the length of the trunk at right angles to the stump but avoiding it. If the wood still needs to be reduced in size, chop down across both the main stem and stump at the same time. This is the most likely run of the grain, and you will separate the wood into two Y-shaped halves.

Keep your feet well back. Nothing upsets the rhythm of work more than ugly chunks of timber spinning back and taking chips out of your ankles. The snags which most often crop up

135

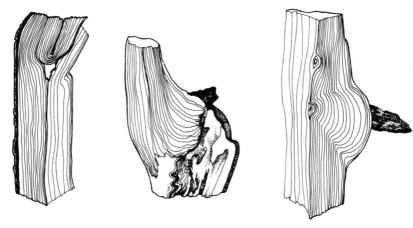

Some awkward knots

are knots, stumps where branches once joined on, sodden wood and twisted grains. The remedy for every one of these is the same: the hammer and the wedge.

The routine goes something like this: you are thunking away with the axe as hard as you can go. The blade penetrates so far and will go no further. You thump the wood hard on the ground or chopping block, and all that happens is that it bounces right back up again. No penetration is taking place. By now, the axe head is firmly wedged in the wood and as likely as not will refuse to allow itself to be removed. Let it be. Fool the damn thing and find a use for it.

Lay the log on the ground. From the point where the axe head has made some entry there will be a split running along the length of the trunk. It may be a large split, it may be a minute one, but there will be some kind of break.

Take a wedge and insert it beyond the axe blade, into the split. Tap it into place with the hammer. Then using the upright handle of the jammed axe to hold the wood steady, whang into the wedge with your hammer, driving the wedge down into the wood. Gradually, the wood will come apart and the split widen. Here, you are likely to hear the phenomenon known to foresters and other log splitters as 'the wood talking to me'.

The form this talk takes is a cracking, splitting kind of sound that continues after you have stopped bashing the wedge. You pause to get your breath and down at your feet the wood continues to splutter and snap. This indicates that you are winning. The wood is giving you best and slowly coming apart at the seams. A few more sturdy blows of the hammer and the battle will be won.

The worst wood to deal with is sodden wood. After you have sawn it to length you may still be unable to get into it any further. The wetness makes the wood so elastic that even though you wham down on it with your axe with every ounce

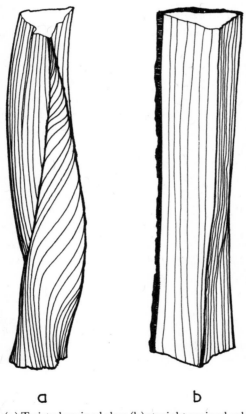

a   b

(a) Twisted grained elm; (b) straight grained oak

137

you can give it, the blade just bounces back without making a bite. In extreme cases, every time this happens, a shower of moisture will spurt from the side of the wood. If you then attempt to tackle it with the wedge, you may be no more successful. The wedge blade will jump out of the wood every time you hit it without gaining a purchase.

There is only one desperate remedy. You must saw the wood into shorter lengths so that the binding power between the wood fibres is, in the shorter size, reduced sufficiently for the axe to begin to work them apart. Even so, wet wood is a bit of a back breaker. Wood in that condition is best left for a few weeks to dry out somewhat before you tackle it. Even then it may be tricky. (However, you still have to air-dry it in your wood pile for a minimum of six months after cutting). It is useful to have two sizes of wedge: a stumpy one with a 1-inch (2·5 centimetre) blade and a heftier one with a 4-inch (10-centimetre) blade, called a bolster.

In the case of wood with a thick series of tough knots, or a gathering of fibres where two branches came together, or, as in the case of elm, where the grain twists right down through the length of the wood, it may be necessary to set to work in a piecemeal way.

You make a start with the axe as I have described. Then work in the first wedge. Once this has bitten, the axe will come free. But still the split does not extend more than an inch or so

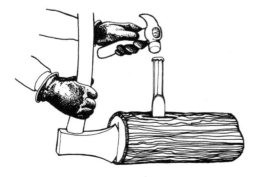

The hammer and wedges

138

The upside-down axe method

beyond the wedge. This is where you bash in the second wide-blade wedge so that the wood continues to split along the same line of grain. When this second wedge is into the wood and the split opened a fraction more, the first wedge will come free. Insert this to continue the split, and so on right along the length of wood. In some really recalcitrant cases the wood won't come apart until the very last inch. But you have the consolation of knowing that you will always win in the end. The log to defeat you hasn't yet been grown.

But be forewarned, this is tough work for which you will have to sink down on your knees – not to pray, but to work up a heavier thump.

For cases where the axe is stuck firmly in the wood a friend of mine has worked out an alternative method. It hasn't proved very helpful in my hands, but then mine are rather unhelpful hands at the best of times. I pass it along for what you can make of it.

The theory is – and maybe, the practice also – that the lump of wood in which the axe is lodged must be heavier than the axe, and therefore, possesses the greater inertia. So you upend things – the axe underneath the wood – then bash the axe-and-wood combination fiercely on the ground, and because the wood weighs more than the axe head the wood will drive into the axe harder than the axe would have driven into the wood the other way up – if you see what I mean.

I have a feeling the thinking is sound. But I find the upside-down mass so top-heavy and awkward to control that I get better service from the traditional arrangement. But if you have thicker wrists than mine, perhaps you can make this work.

In one corner of your work space – you seem to need more and more space the longer this wood-cutting programme goes on – it is helpful to have a largish box. A tea chest or one of those sturdy wooden boxes that removal men use to pack odds and bobs into – come to think of it, they use tea chests as well.

Apart from your large wood, your medium wood and the small wood, you will require quantities of kindling, the amount depending on how often you light your various wood stoves. If you keep your main stove in the whole time, you won't need to relight it very often!

During the cutting operation, you will continually be trimming off small ends, stumps, twigs and other broken pieces. If you toss these into a large box you will gradually build up a good collection of kindling. Otherwise, the bits drop on the floor, make a mess, get damp and are thereby good for nothing except to house insects.

The other by-product you will accumulate is a mess of twigs, usually in the form of top ends of trees. When you have started at the base of the trunk, cutting away the roots – also good for burning – first you will cut large wood, then the medium and small stuff. As you work up along the tree bole, the sections get smaller and thinner, until you are left with the top mass of small twigs. Pile these in one of the ten or twelve corners your work space has by now acquired, and when you want kindling, snip into these with ordinary garden pruning shears. A cardboard apple carton, the sort with holes in the sides so that air can

140

circulate, is quite useful for keeping a supply of fire-lighting wood in dry condition.

Wood is the wood-stove burner's badge of membership, so let us have a look at what he is getting for his regular subscription to the club.

7

NEXT WOODS

This book began with a personal declaration. It ends with a confession. I cannot tell one wood from another. Or, hardly. There are well-informed persons who come across my wood pile, pointing out the sycamore, elm, oak, beech and other assorted varieties. To me they are all just bits of wood that I cut down, dragged in, chopped or sawed, and stacked. They are bits that I am going to burn.

And this is where we come to the heart of the matter. In earlier times little rhymes were common currency among country residents as a mnemonic to remind them of the good burning woods, the bad woods, and the differing characteristics of those average woods between. I can now comfortably report that in the modern, efficient wood-burning apparatuses that are the *raison-d'être* of this book, it makes hardly a jot or tittle of difference. All woods burn.

Just the same, if only so that sensible wood mixes can be put together in the stove for effective combustion, some process of categorisation has to be thought out.

My schema, a most simple one, is that one grades the various woods by density. Soft, or coniferous woods, will tend to weigh light. Hard or broad-leaf woods will weigh on the heavy side. With this simple formula in mind, all woods can be graded for burning just by lifting and assessing the weight for the size in question.

The significance of doing this is that, as a generalisation, soft woods burn more quickly than hard woods. At the same time, however, they burn with a higher, more intense heat. Some soft woods spit, so when you are planning your fire management for the day or evening, you scan the wood available to you in the fire box to see in what order it is best to load the logs.

Soft woods are best for lighting the fire, they catch more readily and the flame spreads more rapidly across them. Once alight, the heavier, slower burning hard woods can be dumped on top.

This knowledge is also useful in deciding what trees to grow – should you happen to be in a growing mode – or which to cut, drag in and store if that is the way of your wood-working life. When wood is on offer for purchase, you can judge how much you should pay for what woods by knowing what use you can make of coniferous and deciduous trees.

Having said that, there is no essential difference in the regimen you impose on your wood supplies. All trees have to be cut and the logs air dried. Perhaps soft woods may dry out somewhat more rapidly than hard wood, but in practice you are going to give each type a good six months of air drying in your stack, as a minimum.

As wood burning catches on, and some kind of organisation designed for the distribution of wood fuels on a national scale comes into being, it is likely that new types of wood fuel will come on the market. It is impossible to anticipate every eventuality. But there are two kinds of wood fuel that I would like to plonk my money down on. My decision to do so in both cases stems from the same reason.

It has to be admitted that, commercially speaking, wood fuel suffers a grave disadvantage. It is a bulky, awkward item to transport, and because of this, the cost of moving it from forest to wood stove is high. There are two ways of overcoming this that I suspect may find more public favour in the future because, while cutting down on the transport cost problem, they dig equally into other wood fuel difficulties.

My first candidate is charcoal, which is not, as you will instantly point out, a new fuel, but one that has been around for a few thousand years. The Chinese, who seem to have done almost everything first except explode H-bombs and fly Concorde, certainly were strong on charcoal well BC.

In our less well-informed times, charcoal has sunk to the level of a cosmetic fuel, being humped home in small paper bags and used to cook to an ash-blackened consistency – rather like charcoal itself – bootleather steaks on the back-garden barbecue.

In Africa where they have a bit more of the proper sense of things than we do, charcoal is a natural fuel. For us, its advantages are that it is efficient, its calorific value is higher than raw wood, it is less bulky and therefore proportionately cheaper to transport. And it is smokeless and able thereby to overcome the objections of even the most recalcitrant and hidebound Department of the Environment person. If renewable wood fuel derivatives can be brought back to use in the heart of modern cities, this is an obvious step towards the return of civilised living in those parts. Moreover, it is conveniently storeable and fits in with modern flab-man's reluctance to harden his hands with rough sawing.

Also in that category are wood briquettes. One of the hindrances to an orderly wood-fuel life that crops up at the supply end of things is the maddening insistance of trees on the production of large quantities of twigs and other wood bits. If only trees could be encouraged not to do this, it would make everything so much simpler for those of us trying to nudge along the wood-burning activity. Alas, trees do their own thing, and all we can do is try to come to grips with them.

One coming-to-grips remedy is on-site wood briquetting. The process, so far as I can discover, dates back to 1856 and a certain F. N. C. Clarke. English, naturally.

The method he devised, and the machine he built to carry it out, are both relatively simple. When items are squashed by the application of extremely high pressures, they get hot. If wood is subjected to a pressure of up to 10 tonnes per square inch it becomes so hot that the natural resins and other binders in the wood melt or, as they say in the trade, 'plasticize'. When the pressure is released, these resins harden again and bind the wood into whatever form it took under pressure. There are currently two machines available on the world market. One is the 'Glomera' from Switzerland; the other, aptly named 'Pres-to-log', comes from the USA. Both work in the same way.

Scrap wood of almost any size or quality is reduced to

sawdust and fed to a pressure chamber where the squeezing, heating and plasticizing programme I have already outlined takes place. From the back end of the machine a continuous tube of wood fuel is pushed out and cut into handy log lengths. In America, these are made up into 'Cellopac' bundles of six or a dozen and sold in supermarkets.

There is no reason why fuel of this type cannot be moulded and cut into any required shape or size. It can be made to fit automatic feed hoppers – allowing wood-burning persons to wine and dine themselves with friends until the small hours of the night without having the faintest fear that the fire will have gone out and all life-support systems come to a halt by the time they return home. When wood burning and civilised living run hand in log box, you certainly have something, my friend, you certainly have.

Oddly, wood briquetting has never found favour in Britain. A diligent search through the archives of TRADA (Timber Research and Development Association) uncovers scads of material on wood briquetting programmes in other lands. 'However', ends an acidulous and curt note, 'these methods have never been found to be practicable in the UK.'

I have found just one company in England that is looking at the possibilities of marketing wood briquettes here. Its managing director informed me: '. . . we have recently turned our attentions to the question of wood-waste briquettes. As we are in the very early stages with this, I do not think that we can provide any information which would be helpful . . .' Perhaps by the time this book comes out, something helpful will have emerged.

Well that is the wood-burning case. As I close these pages, winter is galloping in from the wings. While the temperature drops, my wood pile rises, as I saw and chop against the day of fuel judgement.

At least I have no worries about supplies. At least I know I am not despoiling the atmosphere, nor ruining the environment. This year's growth has already overrun all I cut last year. Next year's will cover everything I am cutting now.

ACKNOWLEDGEMENTS

When a non-technical author, as I am, gets himself enmeshed in a subject like this, it is somewhat like putting up a tent for the first time. Pretty soon one needs a helping hand, and I am very fortunate that a large number of helpful hands have been offered to me, and those offers gratefully taken up.

So let me here honour my obligations by setting up my own celebratory tree trunk and carving their names upon it:

Miss S. E. Dobson, Department of the Environment
Miss Jane Dunmore, Information Officer, National Society
for Clean Air
Miss Susan Forester, Secretary, The Tree Council
Mr. R. M. Harley, Managing Director, Dartington
Woodlands Ltd
Mr E. H. M. Harris, Director, Royal Forestry Society
Mr W. M. Ingram, Director, Asthall Holdings Ltd
Mr Anthony Marriage of Uplyme
Mr C. S. Mitchell, Director, South West Woodburning
Centre
Mrs A. E. Peters, Librarian, Timber Research and
Development Association
Major-General T. A. Richardson, Assistant Secretary,
Timber Growers' Organisation Ltd
Mr Andrew Saye, Managing Director, Logfires
(Woodstoves) Ltd
Mr Simon Thorpe, Managing Director, Simon Thorpe Ltd
Mr P. L. Tindall, Director, S.I.P. Wood Processing Ltd
Mr P. J. Wood, Senior Research Office, Department of
Forestry, University of Oxford

When the gales raged and a mess of tent flaps and tangled ropes had collapsed around me, two utterly kind persons went far beyond all reasonable calls on their time by reading and correcting those chapters dealing with matters of which they have expert knowledge and experience. However, such are the wilful ways of authors who will insist on putting in bits despite the care of the most alert and attentive mentor, errors occur. Wherever this has happened let me absolve entirely my patient helpers. They did their very best for me. But, the blames are all mine.

I can only record my debt to them by carving their names in the place of esteem and respect on my tree:

Mr E. A. Keen, District Officer, Forestry Commission, Devon District

Mr Simon Keeping, Managing Director, Simon Keeping (Developments) Ltd

USEFUL ADDRESSES

UK Manufacturers of Wood Stoves

The Broomside Foundry Co (1922) Ltd, Bonnybridge, Stirlingshire FK4 2EN

Enfield Foundry Co Ltd, 25 York Road, Waltham Cross, Hertfordshire

Euro-Heat Ltd, Fearnley House, 70/72 Fearnley Street, Watford, Hertfordshire WD1 7DE

Farm 2000 Ltd, 15 Hazelbank, Kings Norton, Birmingham B38 8BT

Haymarket Stores, 4 Market Street, Hay-on-Wye, Hereford HR3 5AF

Home Stoves Ltd, 113 Warwick Avenue, Maida Vale, London W9 2PP

Wade Lewis Ltd, Stewart House, Brook Way, Kingston Road, Leatherhead, Surrey KT22 7LY

Logfires (Woodstoves) Ltd, The Estate Yard, Bishop's Canning, Nr Devizes, Wiltshire

Philip Spencer Stoves Ltd, Cherrycourt Way, Stanbridge Road, Leighton Buzzard, Bedfordshire

Scanfield Boilers Ltd, Ham Street, near Ashford, Kent TN26 2HG

Smith & Wellstood Ltd, Bonnybridge, Stirlingshire FK4 2AP, Scotland

Waterford Ironfounders Exports Ltd, New Cut Lane Industrial Estate, Woolston, Warrington WA1 4AQ

A. J. Wells & Sons, Crocker Lane, Kingates, Niton, Isle of Wight PO38 2NT

Woodwarm Stoves, Simon Keeping (Developments) Ltd, Bridge Works, Bridge Street, Uffculme, Cullompton, Devon

Importers of Foreign Wood Stoves

A. Bell & Co Ltd, Kingsthorpe, Northampton NN2 6LT

Chaskit, Chaskit House, Langton Green, Kent TN3 0EG

The Cheshire Woodstove Company, 36 Watergate Row, Chester

Copco International Inc, 45 Castle Street, High Wycombe, Buckinghamshire

Euro-Heat Ltd, Fearnley House, 70/72 Fearnley Street, Watford, Hertfordshire WD1 7DE

Jetmaster Fires, 36 St George's Street, Winchester, Hampshire SO23 8BE

Le Feu de Bois Ltd, 14 Church Street, Twickenham, Middlesex TW1 3NJ

Lodebrook Ltd, Watergate Lane, Bulford, Salisbury, Wiltshire SP4 9DY

Modern Fires Ltd, 50 Brighton Road, Salfords, Redhill, Surrey

Morley Marketing, Morley Hall, Ware, Hertfordshire SO12 7QP

Philip Spencer Stoves Ltd, Cherrycourt Way, Stanbridge Road, Leighton Buzzard, Bedfordshire

Strax Distribution Ltd, 41b Brecknock Road, London N7 0BT

Ellis Sykes & Son Ltd, Victoria Works, Howard Street, Stockport, Cheshire

Simon Thorpe Ltd, New Road, Newcastle Emlyn, Dyfed, Wales SA38 9BA

Tinderpost Ltd, P.O. Box 78, Folkestone, Kent CT20 1UL

U. A. Engineering Ltd, Canal Street, Sheffield S4 7ZE

Yorkpark Ltd, Woodbridge, Chequers Lane, Prestwood, Buckinghamshire HP16 9DR

INDEX

151

152